BeHavioraL OBJecTives

A GUIDE TO INDIVIDUALIZING LEARNING

maTHemaTICS

JOHN C. FLANAGAN
ROBERT F. MAGER
WILLIAM M. SHANNER

Westinghouse Learning Press
Palo Alto, California

Division of Westinghouse Learning Corporation

contents

Preface

A huge advantage of an instructional objective derives from the simple fact that it is written. Once it is written, it is visible. Once it is visible, it can be reviewed, evaluated, modified, and improved.

Objectives are frequently discussed but seldom seen. In these volumes you can see approximately four thousand instructional objectives in the subject areas of language arts, mathematics, science, and social studies ranging from grade one through grade twelve. This collection represents the cooperative efforts of over one hundred classroom teachers and an almost equal number of staff members at the American Institute for Research and Westinghouse Learning Corporation.

Since these volumes present written objectives rather than a discussion about objectives, they become the criteria by which materials are selected, content outlined, instructional procedures and educational technology developed, and tests and examinations prepared. All these aspects of an educational program are really the means for accomplishing the basic educational purpose.

This collection serves to stimulate teachers and educators in selecting and developing behavioral objectives for their own use. These objectives may be criticized and evaluated, revised and modified; objectives may be added or deleted, all with the purpose of arriving at an appropriate set of educational outcomes to meet the educational needs of a local situation and of individual students.

The rather obvious purpose of an instructional objective should be to make clear to teachers, students, and other interested persons what youngsters should be able to do as a result of the instructional program. A well-written instructional objective should specify under what conditions and to what extent a certain kind of student performance can be expected.

Unfortunately, school systems commonly lack a comprehensive and reasonably consistent set of educational objectives. Educational goals and objectives are frequently expressed only in broad, global terms, and the question of what and how to teach is left to a considerable extent to the teacher. As a result, quality in the schools is closely associated with the qualified and skillful teacher. No doubt considerable excellent educational work is done by artistic teachers who, while they may not have a clear conception of goals, do have an intuitive sense of good teaching. Their materials are significant, and they develop topics effectively with students. They clarify the educational objectives (even objectives not directly stated) through their actions as they teach intuitively.

If the foregoing were to serve as a basis for defining education, then the "intuitiveness of the artistic teacher" would have to be built into the educational program. This, of course, cannot be done. The alternative is to start with clearly defined, rather than implied, instructional objectives.

Educational objectives—even clearly stated, specific objectives —are, in the final analysis, matters of choice and thus are value judgments. The question then arises:

> Who provides these value judgments? In the last analysis, the public schools are operated to meet the needs of society. Some of the objectives, along with rules regarding who shall attend school, are provided for in state constitutions and by-laws. Other objectives are set forth by the efforts of elected representatives of the people of a community. Some are provided by professional educators hired to operate the schools. Still others come from our knowledge of children themselves and how they learn. All of these sources effectively furnish the educational objectives for a local public school. Objectives will change with the changing conditions of the times, sometimes quickly, as with Sputnik, but usually slowly.

In evaluating and summarizing instructional objectives, whatever their source, certain kinds of information and knowledge provide a more intelligent basis than others for making decisions about objectives. If certain facts are known and understood, the probability is increased that judgments about objectives will be wise and that educational goals will gain in significance, objectivity, and validity. For this reason the so-called scientific study of the curriculum has largely concerned itself with investigations that may provide a more adequate basis for wise selection of instructional objectives than has previously been available.

What sources can be used for acquiring information from which objectives can be derived? This question has been the subject of much controversy between essentialists and progressives, between

PREFACE

subject specialists and child psychologists, between sociologists and philosophers, between this school group and that school group.

Progressives and child psychologists emphasize the importance of studying the child to find out what kinds of interests he has, what problems he encounters, what purposes he has in mind. They see this information as providing the basic source for selecting objectives. Essentialists and subject specialists, on the other hand, are impressed by the large body of knowledge collected over many thousands of years, the so-called cultural heritage, and emphasize this body of knowledge as the primary source for deriving objectives. They view objectives as essentially the basic learnings selected from the vast cultural heritage of the past.

Many sociologists and others concerned with the pressing problems of contemporary society see in an analysis of today's world the basic information from which objectives can be derived. They view the school as the agency for helping young people to deal effectively with the critical problems of life in modern society. If existing problems can be determined, then, the sociologist feels, the objectives of the school are to provide the knowledge, skills, and attitudes that will help people to deal intelligently and effectively with contemporary problems. On the other hand, educational philosophers recognize that there are basic values in life, largely transmitted from one generation to another by means of education. They see the school as aiming essentially at the transmission of basic values derived by comprehensive philosophic study; hence they view educational philosophy as the source from which objectives can be derived.

The point of view recommended here is that no single source of information is adequate as a basis for wise and comprehensive decisions about the objectives of education. Each of the sources described has certain values to commend it. Each source should be given consideration in planning. In this way educational programs may be developed that are flexible and suitable for any specific public-school situation, regardless of whether that situation is influenced primarily by a single viewpoint or by a combination of attitudes concerning educational objectives.

Although the objectives in these volumes contribute to solving the difficult problem of delineating a curriculum, they should not be considered as a final and perfect product. Any set of objectives must in fact be considered tentative, requiring continuous updating and reevaluation to the educational purposes and programs at hand. To have critical comments made about one's objectives should be taken as a compliment, since criticism can only be made when one has given the thought and taken the time to write the objectives down.

In spite of the great effort and the number of man-hours that have gone into the task of compiling the objectives in these volumes, several of the objectives listed cannot yet be considered to be "true objectives," if by objectives we mean instructional outcomes described in terms of performance. In fact, the editors wish to make the following comments as to why some of the objectives herein are open to multiple interpretation.

1. Some objectives describe a classroom activity taking place during the process of learning, rather than the performance to be exhibited by the proficient student after learning.

2. Some objectives lack a description of, or even a suggestion for, the stimulus conditions under which a student is to perform. Conversely (and perversely), seemingly unimportant stimulus conditions are occasionally included.

3. Some statements (this term seems more appropriate here than objectives) fail to suggest any sort of criteria. Though not all objectives demand criteria, this lack makes for a certain vagueness in the phrasing of some objectives.

With slight editorial and organizational modifications, the objectives in these volumes are the objectives for Project PLAN. Project PLAN is a system of individualized education, operative at grades one through twelve in the subject areas of language arts, mathematics, science and social studies.

Project PLAN was conceived by Dr. John C. Flanagan, and to some extent evolved from the findings of Project TALENT, a large-scale, long-range project involving the collection of comprehensive information about education in the United States. Project TALENT involved the testing of a sample of 440,000 students in 1,353 secondary schools in all parts of the country in March 1960, with subsequent follow-up studies.

PREFACE

Through Dr. Flanagan's efforts, Project PLAN was brought into being in February 1967 as a joint effort of the American Institute for Research, Westinghouse Learning Corporation, and thirteen school districts.[1] Dr. Flanagan has continued to direct the developmental and research work on Project PLAN since that date. Assisting in the developmental work of Project PLAN has been Dr. Robert F. Mager, who is well known for his book *Preparing Instructional Objectives.*[2] Dr. Mager's philosophy was followed in the development of the objectives in these volumes.

The objectives in these volumes, then, have originated from teachers and have been tried out in schools. We wish to acknowledge the efforts of the teachers (their names are listed below) who were assigned by their school districts to work for a year at the American Institute for Research in Palo Alto. Without their contributions these volumes of objectives would not have been possible.

Archdiocese of San Francisco, Department of Education: Sister Maura Cole, Marian Bonnet, Janice Edminster, Sister Charlene Foster, Sister Bernice Heinz, Sister Patricia Hoffman, Sister Mary Vincent Gularte, Sister Anita Kelly, Sister Jeanne Marie Sosic

---

1. Archdiocese of San Francisco, Department of Education, San Francisco, California; Fremont Unified School District, Fremont, California; San Carlos Elementary School District, San Carlos, California; San Jose Unified School District, San Jose, California; Santa Clara Unified School District, Santa Clara, California; Sequoia Union High School District, Redwood City, California; Union Elementary School District, San Jose, California; Bethel Park School District, Bethel Park, Pennsylvania; Hicksville Public School District, Hicksville, New York; Penn Trafford School District, Harrison City, Pennsylvania; Pittsburgh Public Schools, Pittsburgh, Pennsylvania; Quincy Public Schools, Quincy, Massachusetts; Wood County Schools, Parkersburg, West Virginia.
2. R. F. Mager, *Preparing Instructional Objectives* (Palo Alto, Calif.: Fearon Publishers, 1962). The cooperating school districts furnished classroom teachers each year from 1967 through June 1970 to develop the objectives and to prepare the Teaching-Learning Units that enable students to accomplish the objectives. These teachers worked under the supervision of American Institute for Research and Westinghouse Learning Corporation professional personnel. The director of these activities was Dr. William M. Shanner. At the end of each year the teachers returned to their respective school districts to initiate the instructional programs organized from the objectives.

MATHEMATICS

PREFACE

Bethel Park School District: Lora Moroni, Gordon Lepri, James Johnson, Judith Andrews, Flora Belle Faddis, David Loadman, Mary Lou Ertman, Roger Johnson, Robert N. Manson, Anna Marie Kerlin, Frances Chase, Robert M. Caldwell

Fremont Unified School District: Lyndall Sargent, Gail Pagan, Rex W. Estes, Caroline Breedlove, Monique Lowy, Charles Swanson, Eileen Trefz, Robert Fairlee, Beverly Ulbricht, Forrest W. Dobbs, Roy C. Fields, Bertram K. Robarts

Hicksville Public School District: Elayne Kabakoff, Richard C. Leuci, Terrence Boylan, Janet Findlay, Willard Prince, Edward Albert, Phyllis A. Kabakoff, Lawrence Dauch, Gerald Shanley, Marjorie Giannelli, Tom Bannan, Gerard F. Irwin

Hughson Union High School District: Warren Green

Penn-Trafford School District: Gary Fresch, Mary Ann Kovaly, Michael Demko, Jack Reilly, Victor Bohince, David Garvin, La-Velle Hirshberg, R. Bruce Robinson

Pittsburgh Public Schools: Ann Mulroy, Jean Brooke, Kenneth Fraser, Shirley Fullerton, Ruth Aaron, Donald Coudriet, Cecilia Sukits, Carmen Violi, Samuel D. Martin, Paul J. Schafer, Mary South, Patricia Sellars

Quincy Public Schools: Jean Ann MacLean, Priscilla A. Dauphinee, Francis Keegan, Katherine Norris, Dennis Carini, Richard Russell, Stephen Fishman, Jack K. Merrill, Marcia A. Mitchell, Robert J. Mattsson, Margaret E. Flynn

San Carlos Elementary School District: Helen Dodds, Natalie Klock, Edith Bryant, Maxine Ross, Elizabeth Movinski, Martha A. Elmore, Charles B. Whitlock, Betty Lee, Lee G. Jensen

San Jose Unified School District: Allaire Bryant, Rise Berry, Hal Garrett, Kathy Roberts, William Harvel, Judy Opfer, Judi Wells, Don Crowell, Oran T. Adams, Marilyn D. Johnson, Alice S. Anderson, Sylvia Atallah

Santa Clara Unified School District: Nancy Wylde, Ruth Hessenflow, Arthur A. Hiatt, Herman Neufeld

PREFACE

Sequoia Union High School District: Gale Randall, Rex Fortune, Robert W. DuBois

Union School District: Jo Ann Risko, Peggy Schwartz, Rose Yamasaki, Glenn Moseley, Sue Coffin, Tod Hodgdon, Barbara S. Donley, Frank Kelly

Wood County Schools: Roberta Adkins, Mary Rector, Larry Myers, Virginia Haller, John Hoyes, Connie Chapman, Ada Ardelia Price, David V. Westfall, Nancy M. Rice, John W. Apgar

In addition, the contributions of the following persons should be acknowledged. Mary June Erickson, language arts; Josephine J. Matthews, Dr. Marie Goldstein, and Dr. Gordon McLeod, mathematics; Marvin D. Patterson, science; Dr. Vincent N. Campbell, social studies; Sarah M. Russell, primary; Katheryn K. Woodley, Dr. Mary B. Willis, Debbra D. Michaels, performance standards; and Dr. Helen D. Dell, editorial

Final acknowledgment should go to those who use the objectives in these volumes. Objectives alone, an educational program do not make. They provide at best only a framework. The responsibility for the learning must rest on the student, guided by the teacher, and supervised by the school administration.

William M. Shanner

Palo Alto, California
December 15, 1970

INTroDuCTion

Although these volumes are mainly self-explanatory, the reader may find helpful the information that follows. The organization of the objectives is discussed, terms are defined, and the numbering system is clarified.

When a text is made up of many small parts, the constraints of print mean that each item has a fixed position on a page and within a volume, a position that establishes a sequential relationship with all preceding and following items regardless of whether such a relationship is logical or intentional. Since behavioral objectives may potentially be arranged in so many ways, it is important to understand how this collection is arranged and organized to avoid any unwarranted assumption that a prescriptive sequence is being suggested.

The objectives have been organized into four volumes, based on a natural, though often overlapping, grouping of the four major subject areas: language arts, social studies, mathematics, and science. Each volume ranges from Grade 1 through Grade 12. This arrangement is based on the needs of teachers and curriculum designers to perceive the span of a particular subject over the school years. An equally good argument can be made for presenting all the material across subjects for a single age level in one volume to emphasize the interrelatedness of the disciplines. The drawback of this format lies in the wide variations of curricula chosen in different local situations for a given age group. Subject-focused volumes, therefore, seem to be the most useful, with cross-referencing and cross-indexing to relate the subject areas.

Although each volume covers the traditional period from Grade 1 through Grade 12, grouping of objectives into single grade levels is inappropriate, again because of the flexibility of modern curriculum design. Instead, the objectives within each volume have been grouped according to Primary, Intermediate, and Secondary levels. The objectives in these groups overlap to some extent, but use of the three designations divides the objectives into sections of manageable size.

INTRODUCTION

These three groups, or levels, may be roughly defined as follows:

Primary: Primary refers to Grades 1 through 3 and covers the material that, in most cases, is presented in these three years. Some readiness material is included that covers preschool years. The more advanced material may be applicable to the Intermediate level; some objectives from the Intermediate level may be appropriate for late Primary.

Intermediate: Intermediate refers to the years usually included in Grades 4 through 8. Once again, this decision is arbitrary; curricula for Grades 7 and 8 are sometimes closely related to high-school studies. Where a junior high school includes Grades 7, 8, and 9, the Intermediate and the Secondary objectives need to be considered selectively.

Secondary: Secondary designates high school, from freshman through senior years. The material presumes that the student has covered the work included in the earlier grades. There is little or no re-presentation of review topics, nor are there objectives designed for remedial work.

Within subject areas there are many ways to subdivide material. It is important to have enough subdivisions to be meaningful and yet not so many that overlapping and confusion result.

The following lists show the topics selected for each volume.

LANGUAGE ARTS
   Listening Skills
   Speaking Skills
   Reading Skills
   Writing Skills
   Grammar Skills
   Study Skills
   Personal Communication and Development Skills
   History and Dialectology
   Classification, Interpretation, and Analysis of Literary Forms
   Original Writing
   Oral and Dramatic Interpretation
   Critical Analysis of Media

INTRODUCTION

SOCIAL STUDIES
  History
  Sociology and Anthropology
  Political Science
  Geography
  Economics
  Psychology and Philosophy
  Social Studies Inquiry Skills

SCIENCE
  Life Science
    Biology (at secondary level only)
  Physical Science
    Chemistry (at secondary level only)
    Physics (at secondary level only)
  Earth Science
  Science Inquiry Skills

MATHEMATICS
  Analysis of Number and System
  Operations: Numerical and Algebraic
  Operations: Graphics
  Geometry
  Measurement and Probability
  Sets and Logic
  Problem Solving

The topics are useful here, but their sequence has no special significance. A sequence that appears logical to one curriculum designer may seem totally illogical to another. Printed material can never embody the flexibility that is possible in instruction. For example, in *Social Studies* the major topics occur in the same sequence through Primary, Intermediate, and Secondary levels. This sequence by no means implies that history should precede political science or economics in any one of these levels, since much instruction proceeds concurrently in various topics as well as in subject areas.

Another problem in writing objectives lies in breaking the material into appropriate learning "chunks." An objective can be so broad that it is meaningless, or it can represent such a small sample of behavior that the instructional program appears to proceed at a snail's pace.

INTRODUCTION

Behavioral Objectives: A Guide to Individualizing Learning approaches this quandary by selecting major benchmarks in student progress. These have been designated Terminal Objectives; subsumed under these, Transitional Objectives group the Terminal Objectives into smaller units.

A Terminal Objective represents a major growth point in student progress, the culmination of work done over a period of time. It can be tested through a project undertaken by a student as in a social-studies investigation, or it may be measured by a test that presents a variety of problems as defined in the objective.

Transitional Objectives lead the student to mastery of the Terminal Objective. Decisions regarding the amount to be mastered in a Transitional Objective may appear to have been made on an arbitrary basis. Sometimes small categories have been grouped into an objective that represents a fairly large area of behavior. Other objectives may seem overly small. Once again, it must be emphasized that these objectives serve as guidlines, not as prescriptions.

Numbering System: Each Terminal Objective is identified by a subject-area designator—LA for language arts, SS for social studies, MA for mathematics, and SC for science—and a three-digit number. The numbers begin with 005 and continue at intervals of five, with a few exceptions, so that new Terminal Objectives can be inserted without rearrangement of the numbering system. In final editing of these volumes such interpolations were made, and the new numbers were assigned sequentially. In each subject area Primary begins with 005, Intermediate with 200, and Secondary with 500. Since numbers were assigned after the objectives were assembled, they do not represent a prescribed sequence.

For those who are interested in making a more comprehensive numbering system, a two-decimal designator can be added for each of the Transitional Objectives that follows a Terminal Objective. (In the present collection no set of Transitional Objectives exceeds 99.) For computer purposes, each of the lettered subject-area designators may be assigned a number: 1, 2, 3, 4.

In this way a six-digit code can be constructed to identify any objective by subject area or by age group. Addition of a seventh digit would permit identification of the cognitive level as well.

INTRODUCTION

Cross-references: To show the interrelatedness of these objectives, some cross-referencing has been indicated by numbers in parentheses that refer to Terminal Objectives. The letter designator shows whether reference is made to an objective in the same area or to one in another subject area. These cross-references can only suggest the wide possibilities of relating various topics.

Cognitive level: Behavioral objectives are often criticized for their seeming triviality and the fact that many of them call upon memorization and application of learned facts. In an effort to test the objectives in these volumes, a modified approach to Bloom's *Taxonomy of Educational Objectives, Cognitive Domain* was applied, using six cognitive levels. This evaluation proved a revealing indication of how well these objectives are distributed among the cognitive levels. For this reason the cognitive level has been included and is indicated by a roman numeral following each objective.

Each Terminal Objective has been carefully phrased to indicate specifically the cognitive level expected. Transitional Objectives do not follow a rigidly consistent pattern, but wherever possible the verbs were selected from the lists related to the cognitive levels.

The following phrases and verbs have been used:
LEVEL I: KNOWLEDGE. Emphasis is on recall, whether of specifics or universals. Terminal Objective: Show that you know (about) . . .

Transitional Objectives for Level I for the most part use the following verbs: answer questions, choose, define, finish, complete, follow directions, identify, indicate, label, list, locate, match, select.

LEVEL II: COMPREHENSION. Emphasis is on grasp of meaning, intent, or relationship in oral, written, graphic, or nonverbal communication. Terminal Objective: Show your understanding of . . . (by) . . .

In Transitional Objectives the following verbs are used: classify, compare the importance of (not just *compare,* which is Level VI), derive, describe, estimate, expand, explain, express, interpret, measure, put in order, recognize, suggest, summarize, trace, convert, add, balance, calculate, compute, divide, factor, multiply, subtract, write numerals.

LEVEL III: APPLICATION. Emphasis is on applying appropriate principles or generalizations. Terminal Objective: Show that you can use or apply . . .

Transitional Objectives draw mainly on these words: apply, compute, construct, make, draw, demonstrate, differentiate, discuss, express in a discussion, find, use, collect information, keep records, participate, perform, plan, predict, prepare, present, solve (word problems, problem situations), use.

LEVEL IV: ANALYSIS. Emphasis is on breakdown into constituent parts and detection of relationships of the parts and of the way they are organized. This level is often an aid to comprehension or a prelude to evaluation. Terminal Objective: Demonstrate your ability to perceive . . . (the parts of/relationship between) . . . (Words in parentheses can be implied or stated in terms of specifics.)

Transitional Objectives draw from this list: analyze, debate, determine, differentiate, form generalizations, deduce, draw conclusions, make inferences, organize.

LEVEL V: SYNTHESIS. Emphasis is on putting together elements or parts to form a whole not clearly there before the student performance. Terminal Objective: Demonstrate your ability to combine concepts, principles and generalizations.

Transitional objectives usually include one of the following verbs: combine and organize, design, develop, produce, write (an original composition).

LEVEL VI: EVALUATION. Emphasis is on values, making qualitative or quantitative judgments with criteria from internal or external sources and with standards. Terminal Objective: Make a judgment on . . . or involving . . .

Transitional Objectives are built around these verbs: compare (and contrast), make a decision, decide, evaluate.

The reader or user is encouraged to criticize the application of cognitive levels in relation to accuracy of application as well as to appropriateness for the particular topic or age group. Like all other facets of these objectives, the listing of cognitive level is designed to stimulate thought regarding the instructional program.

PRIMARY

analysis of number and system

MA 005   **Show that you can use arabic numerals to count objects and words.   III**

Use the word and symbol for numbers up to 100.   III

Given a group of no more than ten objects, count them.   II

Given groups of objects that contain no more than ten objects, identify the groups from the largest to the smallest and from the smallest to the largest.   II

Recognize the numeral applied to a given set of objects up to 100.   II

Given a point on a number line, write the corresponding number from 0 to 10 for the point.   II

Recognize the relationship between counting numbers and counting objects by counting steps on the number line.   II

Count objects from 0 to 100 orally.   II

Count orally by steps to 100.   II

Write the numeral for a given set of from 0 to 10 objects.   II

Match the word forms of the numbers from 0 to 100 with the correct numerals.   I

List the numbers from 0 to 100 in sequence.   III

List the even numbers from 2 through 100.   III

List the odd numbers from 1 through 99.   III

MA 010   Show that you can use place value to 9999.   II

> Recognize the number of tens and the number of ones in a given 2-digit number.   II

> Recognize the ones, tens, and hundreds places in a 3-digit numeral.   II

> Tell the value of each digit in a 4-digit number.   II

> Rewrite a number with no more than 4 digits, using expanded notation.   III

> Rewrite 3-digit numbers, rounding off to the nearest ten or hundred.   III

MA 015   Show your understanding of the relationship of roman numerals to arabic numerals.   II

> Convert arabic numerals 1 through 39 to roman numerals. Convert roman numerals I through XXXIX to arabic numerals.   II

OPERATIONS: NUMERICAL AND ALGEBRAIC

MA 020   Show that you can use addition by adding 4-digit numbers.   III

> Using a picture of two sets of objects or a number line, add two numbers where the sum is 10 or less.   II

> Add two 1-digit numbers vertically and/or horizontally where the sum is 10 or less.   II

> Add numerals horizontally and/or vertically where the sum is not greater than 18.   II

> Add two 2-digit numerals with regrouping.   II

> Add two 2-digit numerals without regrouping.   II

PRIMARY

Add two 2-digit numerals by using expanded notation.   II

Add two 3-digit numerals with regrouping.   II

Add three 2-digit numerals without regrouping.   II

Find the sums of not more than three addends with not more than three digits in each addend.   II

Add two 4-digit numerals without regrouping.   II

Given the sum and one addend in an addition problem, use inverse operation to find the missing addend.   II

MA 025   Show that you can use subtraction to perform operations with 4-digit numbers.   II

Using a picture of two sets of objects or a number line, subtract a 1-digit number from a larger 1-digit number.   II

Subtract a 1-digit numeral from a larger 1-digit numeral vertically and/or horizontally.   II

Subtract numerals where the minuend is not greater than 18.   II

Subtract 2-digit numerals without regrouping.   II

Subtract 2-digit numerals with regrouping.   II

Subtract a 2- or 3-digit numeral from a 3-digit numeral without regrouping.   II

Subtract a 2- or 3-digit numeral from a 3-digit numeral with regrouping.   II

Subtract 4-digit numerals without regrouping.   II

Find the missing number in an addition or subtraction problem with 2-digit numerals.   II

MATHEMATICS

MA 030   Show that you can use multiplication facts.   III

Add equivalent sets.   II

Recognize a multiplication fact that represents a given repeated addition fact.   II

Multiply two numerals where the product is not greater than 25.   II

Solve word problems using multiplication where the product is not greater than 25.   III

Tell the multiplication facts of 1-digit factors where at least one of the factors is less than 6.   I

Tell the multiplication facts of 1-digit numbers.   I

Find the product of two 1-digit numerals.   II

Multiply a 2- or 3-digit numeral by a 1-digit numeral where regrouping is not required.   II

Multiply a 2- or 3-digit numeral by a 1-digit numeral where regrouping is required.   II

MA 035   Show that you can use division to solve problems with 1-digit divisors.   III

Divide a given set of no more than twenty elements into groups of equivalent sets.   III

Find the quotient of a division problem with a 2-digit dividend and a 1-digit divisor, using repeated subtraction.   II

Divide a 3-digit numeral by a 1-digit numeral (no remainder).   III

Find the quotient and remainder for a division problem with a 2- or 3-digit dividend and a 1-digit divisor.   III

PRIMARY

Write a number sentence for a story problem that requires the division of a 1- or 2-digit number by a 1-digit number. II

MA 040 Show that you can use addition to add like fractions. II

Recognize the fractional numbers $\frac{1}{2}$, $\frac{1}{3}$, and $\frac{1}{4}$. II

Identify sets of objects or whole objects divided into halves, thirds, or fourths. II

Recognize the fraction (halves, thirds, fourths, fifths, sixths, or eighths) represented by the shaded region of a given set or figure. II

Add like fractions with denominators of 2, 3, 4, 5, 6, or 8 where both of the addends and the sum are proper fractions. III

OPERATIONS: GRAPHICS

MA 045 Show your understanding of given patterns by reproducing them. II

Copy a given pattern of objects or shapes. I

Complete given patterns of objects. I

After seeing a given pattern of objects that has no more than three parts, reproduce from memory the same pattern of objects. I

Given a series of objects or shapes in a pattern, draw the next step of the pattern. III

MA 050 Show your understanding of the functions of graphs by explaining them. II

Fill in specific data from a bar or picture graph. II.

Construct a picture graph from given data. II

Geometry

MA 055 **Show your understanding of geometric figures and circles by recognizing them.** **II**

Identify like objects.   I

Identify a circle, square, triangle, and rectangle.   I

Identify objects or drawings that are triangles and those that are quadrilaterals.   I

Describe a given geometric figure as open or closed.   II

Describe a given point as inside, on, or outside a figure.   II

measurement and probability

MA 060 **Show that you can use coin values.** **III**

Identify a penny, a nickel, and a dime, and tell the value of each.   I

Find the value of a given group of pennies, nickels, and dimes that totals less than $1.00.   II

Make change from $1.00 for any amount up to $.99.   III

Select combinations of coins for any value up to $1.00.   III

MA 065 **Show that you can apply understanding of time to the minute.** **III**

Recognize the hour and/or half hour as given on a clockface.   II

Demonstrate the telling of time by setting the hands of a clock to a given hour, half hour, and quarter hour.   III

PRIMARY

Recognize the written time (hour, half hour, quarter hour and five minutes) represented on a given clockface.   II

Express time to the nearest minute, using the colon. Use A.M. for morning and P.M. for afternoon in telling time.   II

MA 070   Show that you can use linear measure to 1/4 inch.

Identify inch, foot, yard, and mile.   I

Measure a given object or line segment to the closest inch.   III

Use a ruler to measure objects to the nearest quarter inch.   III

Given a scale, measure distance on a map.   III (SS 045)

MA 075   Show your understanding of temperature readings.   II

Record the temperature shown on a Fahrenheit thermometer.   II

Find the difference between two given temperatures.   II

MA 080   Show your understanding of weight and liquid measurements.   II

Identify measures used for weight (ounce, pound, ton).   I

Identify measures used for liquid (ounce, pint, quart, gallon).   I

Identify measures used in cooking (teaspoon, tablespoon, cup).   I

sets and logic

MA 085   Show that you can use facts pertaining to elements of a set.   III

Using arrays, find the crossing points through 10.   III

Recognize the smallest or largest object in a group of objects.   I

MATHEMATICS

Given a group of objects, recognize objects that are the same size, the same shape, or the same color.   II

Given groups of objects, recognize the groups that have the same number of objects.   II

Recognize which of two groups of objects has more elements and which has fewer elements.   II

Arrange sets from the smallest to the largest and from the largest to the smallest.   III

Recognize the similarities of given objects.   II

Given a group of objects with one object different from the rest, recognize the object that is different.   II

Recognize the subsets of a given set.   II

Describe the union of two sets.   II

Recognize a group of objects that have something in common.   II

Add equivalent sets.   III

Add disjoint sets.   III

MA 090   Show that you can use set notation to solve simple problems.   III

Recognize a number as being greater than, equal to, or less than a second number.   II

Express two sets of elements in set notation and conclude whether the two sets are equivalent.   III

Express the empty set.   II

Express subsets.   II

Express the union of sets.   II

Express the intersection of sets.   II

Problem Solving

MA 095 Show that you can write number sentences (equations). III

Write a number sentence for a given pictured addition or subtraction problem. III

Write an equation for a pictured addition problem where the sum of the numerals is not greater than 18. III

Write an equation for a pictured subtraction problem where the minuend is not greater than 18. III

Given an addition sentence with two addends and the sum, write an equation for a subtraction problem, using the same numerals. The numerals are not to be greater than 10. III

Recognize the correct symbol ($<$, $=$, or $>$) that belongs between two given numerals when neither numeral has more than 3 digits. II

Write number sentences using 3-digit numerals and the symbols $<$, $=$, and $>$. III

MA 100 Show that you can solve simple word problems. III

Solve word problems in which two 1-digit numbers are added and the sum is 10 or less. III

Solve word problems for addition problems where the sum is not greater than 18. III

Solve word problems for subtraction where the minuend is not greater than 18. III

Solve word problems involving addition and subtraction of two 2-digit numerals. III

Solve to the nearest minute 1-step addition and subtraction story problems involving time. III

Solve word problems in which two 1-digit numbers are added. III

Solve word problems for addition and subtraction of two numerals, each of which has no more than 4 digits.   III

Solve word problems in which a 1-digit numeral is subtracted from a larger 1-digit numeral.   III

MA 105   Show that you can write and solve number sentences for simple word problems.   III

Given addition and subtraction story problems, write them as number sentences. Numbers should be limited to 3 digits.   III

Write a number sentence for a story problem that requires the division of a 1- or 2-digit number by a 1-digit number.   III

Write and solve equations for story problems requiring addition or subtraction.   III

INTERMEDIATE

analysis of number and system

MA 200 **Show that you can use early number systems by expressing symbols of one system in symbols of another system.   III**

> Express Egyptian number symbols as equivalent arabic number symbols.   II

> Express Babylonian number symbols as equivalent arabic number symbols.   II

> Express roman number symbols as equivalent arabic number symbols.   II

> Given a list of numbers orally or in writing, write the equivalent roman numerals up to 5000.   II

MA 205 **Show that you can use place value to 10 digits.   III**

> Recognize the place value of each digit of a number to the millions place.   II

> Give a numeral to hundred millions, express the numeral orally and write it in word form. Given the word form of a number to hundred millions, read the word form and write its numeral name.   II

> Describe the place value of each digit of a number to billions and give the digit's value in expanded form.   II

> Given an oral or written list of numbers to billions, write the numerals.   III

MA 210 **Show that you can identify the properties of whole numbers and apply these properties to problems.   III**

> Demonstrate that the order in which you add two whole numbers does not change the answer.   III

Demonstrate that the way in which you group whole numbers in an addition problem does not change the answer.   III

Demonstrate that subtraction undoes addition for whole numbers.   III

Demonstrate that the order in which you multiply two whole numbers does not change the answer.   III

Demonstrate that the way you group whole numbers in a multiplication problem does not change the answer.   III

Demonstrate that division undoes multiplication for whole numbers.   III

Demonstrate that adding two whole numbers and then multiplying the answer by a third whole number gives the same answer as multiplying each of the first two whole numbers by the third whole number and then adding the two answers.   III

Demonstrate whether the operations of addition and subtraction are commutative and associative.   III

Demonstrate whether the operations of multiplication and division are commutative and associative.   III

Solve a problem involving the distributive law for multiplication over addition and subtraction.   II

Solve a problem involving the distributive law for division over addition and subtraction using 1-digit divisors.   II

Demonstrate whether the operations of addition and subtraction have an identity element.   III

Demonstrate whether the operations of multiplication and division have an identity element.   III

MA 215   Show that you can apply the techniques necessary to write mathematical expressions in simplest terms.   III

Given mathematical expressions that contain parentheses and/or brackets, express them in simplest terms.   II

INTERMEDIATE

Given any simple mathematical sentence using $>$, $<$, $\geqslant$, $\leqslant$, $\neq$, or $\approx$, recognize whether the sentence is true or false. II

MA 220   Show your understanding of proper and improper fractions.   II

Tell what the parts of a fraction symbol represent.   I

Write the fraction symbol for a given part of a whole.   II

Recognize that a given fraction is the same as a given picture of the fraction.   II

Given a picture or diagram that is shaded to show a simple fraction, recognize the fraction shown.   II

Find the value of a specified fractional part of a set or a whole number.   II

Recognize the numerator and the denominator in a given fraction.   II

Given a picture or diagram that is shaded to show a mixed number, recognize the mixed number shown by the shading.   II

Given an improper fraction, express the fraction as a mixed number. Given a mixed number, express the number as an improper fraction.   II

Write the fraction that expresses the relationship between part of a line segment and the whole segment.   II

Given a point on a divided line segment that is one unit long, write a fraction that the point represents.   II

Write an improper fraction for a given picture that shows a fraction greater than 1.   II

Express a given improper fraction as a whole number and a fraction.   II

Given two different fractions, each of which is less than 1, write the fractions in order on the number line.   II

Given a point to the left of 1 on the number line, write at least three fractions that name that point on the number line.   II

Write at least three fractions for a given whole number on the number line.   II

Write a fraction for a given point to the right of 1 on the number line.   II

MA 225   Show that you can apply an understanding of equivalent fractions.   III

Given a picture that shows a fraction and its fraction symbol, demonstrate your knowledge of fractions by dividing the picture into smaller equal parts and writing the new symbol.   III

Given a line segment divided into equal parts and a fraction symbol that names a section of the segment, demonstrate your knowledge of fractions by dividing the line segment into smaller equal parts and writing the new symbol.   III

Write a set of at least three fractions that are equal to each other by multiplying the top and bottom of a given fraction by the same number.   III

Find a fraction in lower terms equal to a given fraction by dividing the top and bottom of the fraction by the same number.   III

Given a simple fraction, recognize several equivalent fractions.   II

Given a fraction, recognize whether the fraction is in lowest terms. If not, express the fraction in lowest terms.   II

Given an improper fraction, express the fraction as a mixed number, the fractional part of which is in lowest terms.   II

Given two or three fractions with unlike denominators, find the lowest common denominator. Express the fractions using this denominator.   II

Express given fractions in lowest terms.   II

INTERMEDIATE

Find the least common multiple (LCM) of two or three numbers.
II

MA 230   Show your understanding of prime and composite numbers.   II

Given any whole number, recognize whether the number is prime or composite.   II

Given a composite number, find all the ways of writing the number as a product of two factors and list the set of factors.   II

Given any two whole numbers, find the set of factors for each number and find the common factors of the two numbers.   II

Given any two whole numbers, find their greatest common factor.   II

MA 235   Show your understanding of absolute value.   II

Write the absolute value of a given number.   II

Find the distance between points on a number line (subtraction with absolute value).   II

Find the sum of two given integers by following the rules stated in terms of absolute value.   II

Find the product of two given integers by following the rules stated in terms of absolute value.   II

MA 240   Show your understanding of rational and irrational numbers.   II

Given a number line and a set of rational numbers, write the numbers on the number line.   II

Given a description of a set of rational numbers, express that set using set notation.   II

Using the method of averaging, find the rational number that is halfway between any two given rational numbers.   II

Define real numbers and classify given real numbers as rational or irrational.   II

MA 245   Show that you can use exponential notation.   II

Given a number in exponential form, describe the base and the exponent. Write the number as the product of like factors, and find the product.   III

Given a number that can be expressed as a product of like factors, express the number in exponential form.   II

Write a numeral in expanded form by expressing the numeral as the indicated sum of the products of each of its digits and a multiple of ten. Write the numeral for a number given in expanded form.   II

Express numbers in expanded form by using exponential notation.   II

MA 250   Show your understanding of expanded and scientific notation.   II

Write a given numeral to millions in expanded form. Given a number in expanded form, write the numeral.   II

Express in expanded notation any whole number of fewer than 8 digits.   II

Express whole numbers of fewer than 8 digits in scientific notation.   II

Using scientific notation, express the product of two whole numbers, each of which has more than 3 digits.   II

OPERATIONS: NUMERICAL AND ALGEBRAIC

MA 255   Show that you can add and subtract 4-digit numbers.   III

Find the sum of four addends with up to 4 digits each.   II

INTERMEDIATE

Write an equation for a word problem involving addition, and find the answer.   III

Add numbers with 3 or more digits.   II

Find the missing addend in an incomplete addition sentence.   II

Find the difference between two numbers, neither of which has more than 4 digits.   II

Write an equation for a word problem involving subtraction, and find the answer.   III (MA 420)

Subtract numbers with 3 or more digits.   II

Given a word problem involving addition and/or subtraction of whole numbers, write an equation for the problem and solve the equation.   III (MA 420)

MA 260   Show that you can solve multiplication problems with at least 2-digit multipliers.   II

Multiply 1-, 2-, and 3-digit numbers by 10, by 100, and by 1000.   II

Multiply a 2-digit number by a 2-digit multiple of 10.   II

Multiply any two 2-digit numbers.   II

Multiply a 3-digit number by a 2-digit multiple of 10.   II

Multiply any 3-digit number by a 2-digit number.   II

Solve word problems involving multiplication of a 3-digit number by a 2-digit number.   III

Identify the factors and the product in a multiplication problem.   I

Find the product of two or three 1-digit numbers.   II

Solve multiplication problems using the distributive property of multiplication over addition. II

Find the product of a 1-digit number and a 2-, 3-, or 4-digit number. II

Find the product of a 1-digit number and a multiple of 10 or 100. II

Given a one-step word problem requiring the operation of multiplication, write the equation and find the answer, using a 1-digit multiplier only. III (MA 420)

Find the missing factor in a multiplication problem. II

Find the product of two 2-digit numbers. II

Find the product of two 2-digit numbers when both factors are multiples of 10. II

Find the product of a 2-digit number and a 3- or 4-digit number. II

Given a word problem requiring multiplication, write the equation and find the answer. III (MA 420)

Given a two-step word problem requiring multiplication and addition or subtraction, write the equation and find the answer. III (MA 420)

Find the product of two numbers, each number having 2 or more digits. II

MA 265 Show that you can solve division problems with at least 2-digit divisors. III

Identify the divisor, dividend, quotient, and remainder in a division problem. I

Divide any 2- or 3-digit number by any 2-digit multiple of 10. II

INTERMEDIATE

Divide any 2- or 3-digit number by any 2-digit number.   II

Find the missing factor in a multiplication problem.   II

Divide a 1-, 2-, 3-, or 4-digit number by a 1-digit number.   II

Given a 2- or 3-digit dividend and a 2-digit divisor, find the quotient and remainder (if any).   II

Given a 4- or 5-digit dividend and a 2-digit divisor, find the quotient and remainder (if any).   II

Find the quotient for a division problem with a 2- or 3-digit divisor.   II

Given a word problem requiring the operation of division, write the equation and find the solution.   III

Given a two-step word problem involving whole numbers, write the equation and find the solution.   III

MA 270   Show your understanding of estimating answers to problems.   II

Given a numeral less than 1,000,000, express the numeral to the nearest ten, hundred, or thousand.   II

Estimate the answer to an addition or subtraction problem by rounding the addends or subtrahend and minuend to the nearest ten, hundred, or thousand.   II

Round off a given number to a given place.   II

Given a 2-digit divisor, express the divisor to the nearer multiple of 10. Use the divisor to estimate a quotient.   II

MA 275   Show that you can complete operations on integers.   III

Given an integer, recognize whether the integer is less than, equal to, or greater than another given integer.   II

Solve word problems requiring the addition of two integers.   III

Find the difference between two integers.   II

Graph ordered pairs of integers on a coordinate system.   II

Write a set of integers on a number line.   II

Find the coordinate of a given point on a number line when the coordinate is an integer.   II

Using a number line, add any two members of this set: {−20, −19, −18 . . . 18, 19, 20}.   II

Find the sum of two or more integers.   II

MA 280   Show that you can add and subtract fractions.   II

Find the sum of two or more proper fractions with like denominators.   II

Add two or three like fractions and express the sum in lowest terms.   II

Find the sum of two or three mixed numbers with like denominators and express the answer in lowest terms.   II

Given two proper fractions with like denominators, find the difference.   II

Add unlike fractions and express the sum in lowest terms.   II

Find the sum of a whole number and a fraction, or a whole number and a mixed number.   II

Find the sum of two or three fractions or mixed numbers with unlike denominators and express the answer in lowest terms.   II

Given a one-step word problem requiring addition of fractions, write the equation and find the answer in lowest terms.   III

Subtract a fraction from a fraction when regrouping is not necessary and write the difference in lowest terms.   II

INTERMEDIATE

Subtract a fraction from a fraction when regrouping may be necessary and write the difference in lowest terms.   II

Subtract a fraction or mixed number from a whole number and write the answer in lowest terms.   II

Find the difference of two mixed numbers with like denominators and write the answer in lowest terms.   II

Subtract unlike fractions and express the difference in lowest terms.   II

Given two fractions, two mixed numbers, or a mixed number and a fraction with unlike denominators, find the difference and express the answer in lowest terms.   II

Given a one-step word problem requiring subtraction of fractions, write the equation and express the answer in lowest terms.   III (MA 420)

Given a two-step word problem involving addition and/or subtraction of fractions, write the equation and express the answer in lowest terms.   III (MA 420)

MA 285   Show that you can multiply and divide fractions.   III

Multiply fractions or mixed fractions by a whole number and express the answer in lowest terms.   II

Multiply a fraction by a fraction, a fraction by a mixed number, or a mixed fraction by a mixed number, and express the answer in lowest terms.   II

Divide a whole number by a fraction or a mixed number. Divide a fraction or a mixed fraction by a whole number.   II

Divide a fraction by a fraction or a mixed fraction. Divide a mixed fraction by a mixed fraction.   II

Solve division of fraction problems using multiplicative inverses. III

MA 290 **Show that you can demonstrate conversion methods for fractions and decimals. III**

Recognize the place value of each digit in a decimal through thousandths. II

Given any decimal through thousandths, express the decimal in word form. II

Given a decimal through thousandths expressed in word form, express the decimal in numerical form. II

Write any given decimal through hundred-thousandths in word form and in numerical form. II

Express fractions with denominators of 10, 100, or 1000 as decimals. II

Given fractions with denominators that can be expressed as powers of 10 (through 100,000), express the fractions as decimals. II

Express fractional numerals of the form $\frac{a}{b}$ where $a < b$ as decimals. II

Express common fractions of the form $\frac{a}{b}$ that are equivalent to repeating decimals in decimal notation. II

Express fractions whose denominators are not factors of 100 as decimals and percents. II

Express repeating decimals as equivalent common fractions in lowest terms of the form $\frac{a}{b}$. II

Express decimals given in tenths, hundredths, or thousandths as fractions. II

Given any decimals through hundred-thousandths, express the decimals as fractions. II

INTERMEDIATE

Express terminating decimal fractions as common fractions in lowest terms of the form $\frac{a}{b}$.   II

MA 300   Show that you can add and subtract decimals.   III

Express a given decimal to the nearest whole number, tenth, hundredth, or thousandth.   II

Find the sum of five or fewer decimals.   II

Add decimals through hundred-thousandths.   II

Find the difference of two decimals.   II

Subtract decimals through hundred-thousandths.   II

Solve word problems involving addition and/or subtraction of decimals.   III

MA 305   Show that you can multiply and divide decimals.   III

Multiply decimals when one of the factors is a whole number.   II

Multiply decimals when both factors are decimals.   II

Divide a decimal by a whole number.   II

Divide a decimal by a decimal.   II

Divide a whole number by a decimal.   II

Divide whole numbers when the divisor is a larger number than the dividend.   II

Solve word problems that require division of a decimal by a whole number.   III (MA 420)

MA 310   Show that you can solve problems in ratio.   III

Write a ratio to express a comparison of two quantities.   II

INTERMEDIATE

Given a ratio, write several equivalent ratios.   II

Solve word problems that require the use of ratio and proportion. III (MA 420)

MA 315   Show that you can solve problems in percentage.   III

Express fractions whose denominators are factors of 100 as fractions with denominators of 100, as decimals, and as percents. Express whole-number percents as decimals and as fractions in lowest terms.   II

Find the amount when the percent and the number are known. II

Find the percent when the number and the amount are known. II

Express fractional percents as proper fractions.   II

Find the number when the percent and the amount are known.   II

Express any ratio as a percent and express any percent as a ratio in lowest terms.   II

Solve given word problems involving ratio and percents.   III

Solve any given proportion for its missing term.   II

Solve word problems involving percent using proportions.   III

MA 320   Show that you can perform square-root operations by finding the square root of a number.   III (MA 245)

Using a table of whole numbers from 0 to 100 and their squares, find the square or the square root of given numbers.   II

Find by approximation the square root of any number that is the product of two equal factors.   II

INTERMEDIATE

MA 325 Show that you can perform operations on bases other than base ten. III

Count in base two, base three, base four, base five, base six, base seven, base eight, and base nine (base$_2$, base$_3$, base$_4$, base$_5$, base$_6$, base$_7$, base$_8$, base$_9$). II

Given a number in a base less than base ten, express the number as a base-ten number. II

Given a base-ten number, express it as a number in a base less than base ten. II

Write base-two numbers in expanded notation. II

Express base-two numbers in base ten and base-ten numbers in base two. II

Find the sum of numbers in base two. II

Find the difference of two numbers in base two. II

Find the product of numbers in base two. II

Find the quotient of numbers in base two. II

Express base-five numbers in expanded notation. II

Express base-five numbers in base ten, and express base-ten numbers in base five. II

Find the sum of numbers in base five. II

Subtract base-five numbers. II

Find the product of numbers in base five. II

Find the quotient of numbers in base five. II

Express base-eight numbers in base-ten and base-ten numbers in base eight. II

Solve problems with base-eight numbers without converting the numbers to base-ten numbers.   III

Express base ten numbers in base twelve numbers and base twelve numbers in base ten numbers.   II

Add and subtract numbers in base twelve.   II

Multiply and divide numbers in base twelve.   II

Choosing a base that you have not used previously, design a base system that is complete with symbols and operations. Develop and solve problems using the numbers of your base system.   V

MA 330   Show that you can apply elements of finite and nonfinite mathematical systems.   III

Construct the addition table for a given modular arithmetic.   III

Demonstrate the following for a given modular arithmetic.   III
1. Closure for addition
2. Commutative principle for addition
3. Associative principle for addition
4. Identity element for addition

Add two given numbers in a given modular arithmetic.   II

Solve an equation of the type $x + a = b$ in a given modular arithmetic.   II

Subtract two numbers in a given modular arithmetic.   II

Construct the multiplication table for a given modular arithmetic. III

Demonstrate the following for a given modular arithmetic.   III
1. Closure for multiplication
2. Commutative principle for multiplication
3. Associative principle for multiplication
4. Identity element for multiplication

Multiply two numbers in a given modular arithmetic.   II

INTERMEDIATE

Solve an equation of the type $ax = b$ in a given modular arithmetic. II

Divide two numbers in a given modular arithmetic. II

Demonstrate the existence of an additive inverse for each element in a given arithmetic in which the modulus is prime. III

Demonstrate the existence of an additive inverse for each element in a given arithmetic in which the modulus is nonprime. III

Demonstrate the existence or nonexistence of a multiplicative inverse for each element in a given arithmetic in which the modulus is prime. III

Demonstrate the existence or nonexistence of a multiplicative inverse for each element in a given arithmetic in which the modulus is nonprime. III

Describe the relation of primeness of the modulus to the existence of a multiplicative inverse and an additive inverse. II

Define a set of rotations and reflections for an n-sided polygon ($n \leqslant 6$). I

Find the result of combining any two elements in a given system of rotations and reflections of an n-sided polygon ($n \leqslant 6$). II

Demonstrate the associative principle for the operation of combining elements in a given system of rotations and reflections of an n-sided polygon ($n \leqslant 6$). III

Demonstrate whether or not the commutative principle holds for the operation of combining elements in a given system of rotations and reflections of an n-sided polygon ($n \leqslant 6$). III

Determine whether a given set of rotations and reflections for an n-sided polygon constitutes a group under the operation of combining motions. Determine whether the set constitutes an Abelian group. III

Find the inverse for each element in a given system of rotations and reflections of an *n*-sided polygon ($n \leq 6$).   II

Given a definition of an operation other than addition, subtraction, multiplication, or division in a finite mathematical system, find the results of the operation on any two elements.   II

Demonstrate the existence of an identity element for a defined operation other than addition, subtraction, multiplication, or division for a given finite mathematical system.   III

Demonstrate the inverse (if it exists) for each element for a defined operation other than addition, subtraction, multiplication, or division for a given finite mathematical system.   III

Demonstrate that the commutative principle exists or does not exist for a defined operation other than addition, subtraction, multiplication, or division in a given finite mathematical system. III

operations: Graphics

MA 335   Show that you can prepare flow charts to solve given algorithms. III

Describe the meaning of the shapes of boxes in a flow chart.   II

Given a flow chart depicting an algorithm, find the output value that the program computes for a given set of input values. II

Draw a flow chart of the algorithm that would be used to solve a given problem in computation.   III

Describe how each of the following is used in connection with computer programs: (1) loops, (2) iteration, (3) test steps, (4) arrays, (5) subscripted variables.   II

Draw a flow chart that shows a given procedure to be carried out on an array of numbers.   III

INTERMEDIATE

MA 340 **Show that you can explain data presented in graphs and construct graphs to summarize data. III**

Construct a picture graph using data presented in a different picture graph. III

Construct a bar graph from given data. III

Construct a line graph from given data presented in a different line graph. III

Construct a circle graph using given data. III

MA 345 **Show your understanding of graph relations and functions. II**

Find and graph the Cartesian product (A × B) for given sets A and B where sets A and B are composed of integers only. III

Define A × B = B × A for given sets A and B where A = B. Define A × B ≠ B × A for given sets A and B where A ≠ B. II

Given a simple mathematical sentence involving rational numbers such as $n > 2$, graph the solution set for n on a number line. III

Given a compound sentence such as $n < 15$ and $n \geq \frac{2}{5}$, graph its solution set on a number line. III

Given sets A and B where $n(A) \leq 6$ and $n(B) \leq 6$, find and graph a relation defined by a given rule and a given domain. III

Express a given relation using a mathematical sentence. II

Recognize whether a given relation is also a function. II

Graph the relation or the function defined by a given mathematical sentence and a given domain D where D is restricted to integers and $n(D) \leq 10$. III

Geometry

MA 350 **Show your understanding of points, lines, angles, and planes by recognizing and classifying them. II**

Recognize and describe a point, a line, and a plane. II

Recognize and describe a line segment and an angle. II

Recognize and describe parallel lines. II

Given two lines that cross each other, find the equal angles. II

Recognize and describe right angles and perpendicular lines. II

Recognize and construct parallel lines, horizontal lines, vertical lines, slanting lines, and perpendicular lines. III

Classify angles as right angles, straight angles, acute angles, or obtuse angles according to the number of degrees in each angle. II

Classify pairs of angles supplementary or complementary according to their sizes. II

Recognize vertical angles and adjacent angles. II

Given an illustration of a geometric figure, describe the figure using the correct symbols for line, angle, right angle, and triangle. II

MA 355 **Show that you understand the properties of geometric figures by describing and classifying them. II**

Given a drawing or a description of any polygon with no more than four sides, identify the polygon. I

Identify by name all regular polygons that have from three to ten sides. I

Find and describe the vertices and the diagonals of a given polygon. II

INTERMEDIATE

Recognize and describe a right triangle and a parallelogram.   II

Recognize the figure formed by joining the midpoints of the four sides of a given quadrilateral.   II

Identify the following parts of a given circle: (1) center, (2) radius, (3) diameter, and (4) chord.   I

Define *acute triangle, right triangle,* and *obtuse triangle,* and recognize examples of each type.   II

Define *isosceles triangle, scalene triangle,* and *equilateral triangle,* and recognize examples of each type.   II

Recognize given geometric figures as congruent or non congruent.   II

Classify given polygons as convex or concave by examining their diagonals.   II

Find a measurement indirectly by using corresponding sides of similar triangles.   II

MA 360   Show that you can construct and measure geometric figures and models.   III

Find the sum of the measures of the angles of a given triangle or of a given quadrilateral without measuring.   III

Given the radius or the diameter of a circle, construct the circle.   III

Construct a circle through three given points that are not in a straight line. Inscribe a circle in a given triangle.   III

Using a protractor, measure to the nearest degree any given angle from 0° to 180°.   II

Using a protractor, construct right angles, straight angles, acute angles, and obtuse angles of specified degrees, accurate to the nearest degree.   III

Using a protractor and a straightedge, construct and measure angles. The angle measure should be correct to within two degrees.   III

Using a compass and/or a straightedge, find whether two line segments are congruent, whether two angles are congruent, and whether two triangles are congruent.   II

Given the diameter or radius of a circle, use a compass to construct the circle.   III

Using a compass, construct the bisector of a given angle.   III

Given a length of each side, use a compass and a straightedge to construct a triangle.   III

Using a compass and a straightedge, construct the bisector of a given line segment.   III

Using a compass and a straightedge, construct the bisector of any given angle less than 180°.   III

Construct models of these solid figures: sphere, cylinder, cone prism, and pyramid.   III

Construct the seven soma pieces when given pictures of them. III

Given a structure or a picture of a structure of soma pieces, construct a duplicate.   III

MA 365   Show your understanding of geometric figures by finding their perimeters, areas, and volumes.   III

Find the perimeter of any polygon when given the measure of each of the polygon's sides.   III

Given the dimensions of any polygon and the perimeter formula, find the perimeter of the polygon.   III

Given the formula for finding the circumference of a circle and the measure of the circumference, the radius, or the diameter of a circle, find the other two dimensions.   III

INTERMEDIATE

Find the area of a rectangular region when given the lengths of the sides.   III

Given the formula for finding the area of a triangle and the measures of the base and height of a triangle, find its area.   III

Given the formula for finding the area of a parallelogram and the measures of the base and altitude of a parallelogram, find its area.   III

Given the formula for finding the area of a trapezoid and the measures of the bases and height of a trapezoid, find its area.   III

Given the formula for finding the area of a circle and the measure of the radius or of the diameter of a circle, find its area.   III

Find the volume of a cube when given the length of one edge.   III

Find the volume of a rectangular prism when given its dimensions.   III

Given the measures of the height and the radius of the base of a cylinder, find the volume of the cylinder.   III

MA 370   Show that you can demonstrate and apply the Pythagorean Relationship.   III

Using the Pythagorean Relationship, recognize right triangles.   II

Using inductive reasoning (experimental method), derive the Pythagorean Relationship $(a^2 + b^2 = c^2)$.   III

Using the Pythagorean Relationship, find the length of the hypotenuse of a right triangle when the two lengths of the legs are given.   III

Using the Pythagorean Relationship, find the length of one of the legs of a given right triangle when the lengths of the hypotenuse and the other leg are given.   III

Solve word problems that require use of the Pythagorean Relationship.   III

measurement and probability

MA 375 **Show that you can demonstrate an understanding of exactness of measurement. III**

> For each of the following primitive methods of measuring time, identify the difficulties of using each method today: (1) sundial, (2) water clock, (3) hourglass, (4) burning candle. I

> Measure time to a given level of accuracy and record your measures in simplest terms. Express long periods of time in terms of (1) millennium, (2) century, (3) decade, and (4) year. II

> Given a ruler with sixteen divisions to the inch, measure a given line segment to the nearest eighth of an inch. II

> Explain why measurements are not completely accurate and what is meant by standard units of measure. II

> Using English units, make linear measurements to a given level of accuracy and record your measures in simplest terms. II

> Using English units, measure weight to a given level of accuracy and record your measures in simplest terms. II

> Using English units, make liquid measurements to a given level of accuracy and record your measures in simplest terms. II

> Record temperature readings to the nearest degree using the Fahrenheit scale. II

> Classify a given quantity as approximate or exact. II

> Calculate the greatest possible error and precision of given measurements. II

> Calculate tolerances and use tolerance notation (e.g., $3 \pm .4$ in.). II

INTERMEDIATE

Find the relative error of a given measurement, giving the answer as a percent. II

Given a ruler with centimeter and millimeter scales, measure given distances to the nearest millimeter. II

MA 380 Show that you can convert one system of measurement to another system. III

Using a table of liquid measures, express cups as pints, cups as quarts, quarts as gallons, pints as quarts, fluid ounces as cups, and fluid ounces as pints, and vice versa. II

Using a table of weight measures, express ounces as pounds and pounds as tons, and vice versa. II

Express linear measures of inches as feet, inches as yards, feet as yards, and feet as miles, and vice versa. II

Using a table of metric measures, express linear measures of millimeters as centimeters, centimeters as decimeters, decimeters as meters, centimeters as meters, and meters as kilometers, and vice versa. II

Express time given on a 24-hour basis as time on a 12-hour basis, and vice versa. II

Given a table of linear measures including kilometer, hectometer, decameter, meter, decimeter, centimeter, and millimeter, express a given measure as any of the other measures (e.g., millimeters as hectometers). II

Given a table of metric units of mass (or weight), convert an amount in one unit to an amount in any of the other units. II

MA 385 Show that you can use addition and subtraction with measures of time, weight, and capacity. III

Add or subtract measures of time (centuries, years, weeks, days, hours, minutes, and seconds), expressing answers in simplest form. III

INTERMEDIATE

Add or subtract measures of weight (ounces, pounds, and tons), expressing answers in simplest form.   III

Add or subtract liquid measures (fluid ounces, cups, pints, quarts, and gallons), expressing answers in simplest form.   III

Find the sum of three like linear English measures, expressing the answers in simplest form.   III

MA 390   Show that you can demonstrate the theory of probability.   III

Define the following words correctly: *likely, more likely, equal chances, certain, uncertain,* and *impossible.*   I

Using a fraction, express the probability of a given event.   II

Using the notation P(E), express the probability of a given event E.   II

Find P, not E, for a given event E.   II

Using a tree diagram or a table, find all possible outcomes and then find the probability of a given outcome.   II

Find the probability for a compound event of the both/and type or for an event of the either/or type.   II

Perform a probability experiment to count the number of ways that the experiment can turn out.   III

Find the number of ways that 2, 3, or 4 things can be chosen from *n* things ($n \leqslant 6$).   II

Find the number of ways 2, 3, or 4 things can be arranged in different orders.   II

Construct a tree diagram that shows the ways a probability experiment can turn out.   III

Construct an array that shows the ways a probability experiment can turn out.   III

INTERMEDIATE

Using a table of outcomes (an array), predict the result of a probability experiment.   III

Perform a probability experiment requiring from 20 to 30 repeated trials and record the result of each trial.   III

Construct a table showing the results of several repetitions of a probability experiment. Construct a line graph or a bar graph to summarize the data.   III (MA 340)

Given a bar graph representing the results of a probability experiment, describe the data in a written report.   II

Describe all the possible outcomes of an event.   II

Find the probability for each outcome of an event if the outcomes are all equally likely.   III

Find the probability for each outcome of an event if the outcomes are not all equally likely.   III

Given two independent events, A and B, find the probability that a certain outcome of A and a certain outcome of B will both occur.   III

Given the number of favorable events (desired outcomes) and the total number of possible events, find the probability of obtaining a given favorable event.   III

Find the probability of two given favorable events occurring successively when the number of favorable events and the total number of possible events are known.   III

Recognize whether generalizations about a given population from a specific random sample are justified.   II

Using set notation, express all possible outcomes for a given experiment.   II (MA 405)

Use set notation to express a specified event in a given sample space.   II (MA 405)

Using the notation $P(E) = \dfrac{n(E)}{n(x)}$ where $x =$ sample space, $E =$ event, and $P =$ probability, express the probabilities of n dimensional events $(n \leqslant 4)$.   III

Given $P(A)$ and using the principle $P(A) + P(\bar{A}) = 1$, find $P(\bar{A})$.   III

Given two events A and B, mutually exclusive or not, find the probability of $A \cup B$ using the following formula.   III

$$P(A \cup B) = \frac{n(A) + n(B) - n(A \cap B)}{n(U)} = P(A) + P(B) - P(A \cap B).$$

Given events A and B, find whether they are independent by comparing $P(A \cap B)$ with $P(A) \cdot P(B)$.   III

Given two independent events A and B, find the probability of $(A \cap B)$ using the formula $P(A \cap B) = P(A) \cdot P(B)$.   III

Using Pascal's triangle, find the number of combinations of n things taken r at a time $(n \leqslant 10)$.   III

Find the probability of an event that involves permutations or combinations.   III

MA 400   **Show that you can apply the frequencies and measures of central tendency.   III**

Given a set of data, organize the data into intervals and, with tally marks, show the frequency of events.   II

Given a set of data, find the arithmetic mean.   III

Given a set of jumbled (unordered) data, find the median when interpolation is not required.   III

Find the median of a set of data where interpolation is needed.   III

Given a set of data, recognize the mode.   II

Given a set of whole numbers, find the average.   III

seTs anD LoGic

MA 405   Show that you can demonstrate sets and set notation.   III

Given a description of set, including the empty set, write its elements (members) using set notation.   II

Identify and tell the difference between equal sets and equivalent sets.   I

Recognize all the subsets of a set.   II

Describe the set that is the union of two given sets.   II

Describe the set that is the intersection of two given sets.   II

Tell the meaning and give proper notations for the following.   I
1. subset   5. complement of a set
2. proper subset   6. disjoint sets
3. universal set   7. finite set
4. empty set   8. infinite set

Find (1) all the subsets for a given set, (2) two disjoint sets for a given universal set, and (3) the complement of a given set A for a given universal set.   II

Determine which of the following relations describes two given sets.   III
1. One is a subset of the other.
2. One is a proper subset of the other.
3. One is a complement of the other with respect to a given universal set.
4. The two sets represent two disjoint sets.

Given a description of a set of rational numbers, express that set using set notation.   II

Express the intersection of any three sets using Venn diagrams.   II

Using Venn diagrams, express (1) a given universal set, (2) subsets of a given set, (3) two disjoint sets, (4) a given set and its complement, (5) the union of two sets, and (6) the intersection of two sets. II

Use Venn diagrams, express (1) the complement of the union of two sets, (2) the complement of the intersection of two sets, (3) the statement $\overline{A \cap B} = \overline{A} \cup \overline{B}$, and (4) the statement $\overline{A \cup B} = \overline{A} \cap \overline{B}$. II

Using the notation $n(A)$ to represent the number of elements in set A, express the cardinality of given sets and combinations of sets. II

MA 410   Show your understanding of the rudiments of logic as they relate to mathematics.   II

Using inductive reasoning (experimental method) as a logical basis for a solution, solve given mathematical problems.   II

Using deductive reasoning as a logical basis for the solution, solve given mathematical problems.   II

Classify a given problem as an example requiring deductive or inductive reasoning.   II

Classify sentences as simple or compound. Classify compound sentences as conditional, conjunctive, or disjunctive.   II

Infer a conclusion from given premises by use of the "if" rule.   II

Write the denial of a given statement.   II

Derive a conclusion from given premises by use of the "if-then-not" rule.   II

Given a simple statement, recognize its denial and the truth value of the denial.   II

Given two simple statements, recognize a conjunction and the truth value of a given conjunction.   II

Given two simple statements, recognize a disjunction and the truth value of a given disjunction.   II

INTERMEDIATE

Recognize the antecedent and the consequent of a given conditional and recognize the truth value of the conditional. II

Using the following laws and definitions, express the reasons for each step in a given completed proof of a numerical statement: (1) definition of natural numbers >1, (2) commutative laws for $+$ and $\times$, (3) associative law of identity. II

Using the following rules of inference, derive a conclusion from a given list of premises: (1) rule of adjunction, (2) rule of simplification, (3) rule of expansion, (4) OR rule, (5) IF rule, (6) IFN rule. II

Using the following rules of inference, express the reasons for each step in a completed logical proof: (1) rule of adjunction, (2) rule of simplification, (3) rule of expansion, (4) OR rule, (5) IF rule, (6) IFN rule. II

MA 415 **Demonstrate your ability to combine principles, concepts, and generalizations by developing an original finite mathematical system, by listing a set of elements, and by defining an operation on the set for which the set is closed and one for which the set is not closed. V**

Develop an original finite mathematical system by listing a set of elements and by defining an operation on the set for which the set is closed. V

Develop an original finite mathematical system by listing a set of elements and by defining an operation on the set for which the set is not closed. V

Demonstrate whether or not the associative principle holds for any three elements of an original finite mathematical system you have developed. V

Demonstrate the existence or nonexistence of the commutative principle for (1) an operation on the set for which the set is closed in an original finite mathematical system, and (2) an operation on the set for which the set is unclosed in an original finite mathematical system. V

Demonstrate the existence or nonexistence of an identity element for (1) an operation on the set for which the set is closed in an original finite mathematical system, and (2) an operation on the set for which the set is unclosed in an original finite mathematical system.   V

Demonstrate the existence or nonexistence of an inverse for each element in the set for (1) an operation on the set for which the set is closed in an original finite mathematical system, and (2) an operation on the set for which the set is unclosed in an original finite mathematical system.   V

Solve problems using binary operations other than addition, subtraction, multiplication, and division.   III

Solve division of fraction problems using multiplicative inversion. III

Recognize examples of the properties of commutativity, associativity, and distributivity.   II

For a given set of numbers and a given operation, recognize whether the operation is closed for that set.   II

PROBLEM SOLVING

MA 420   Show that you can write and solve equations for word problems. III

Write an equation for a word problem involving addition, and find the answer.   III

Write an equation for a word problem involving subtraction and find the answer.   III

Given a word problem requiring multiplication, write the equation and find the answer.   III

Given a word problem requiring the operation of division, write the equation and find the solution.   III

Given a two-step word problem involving whole numbers, write the equation and find the solution.   III

INTERMEDIATE

Given a word problem involving addition and/or subtraction of whole numbers, write an equation for the problem and solve the equation. III

Given a word problem involving multiplication of whole numbers, write an equation for the problem and solve the equation. III

Given a word problem involving division of whole numbers, write an equation for the problem and solve the equation. III

Given a two-step word problem involving addition and/or subtraction of fractions, write the equation and find the answer in lowest terms. III

Draw a diagram for a given word problem. III

Estimate the answer for a given word problem, explaining how you arrived at the estimation. II

Given a word problem, describe the extraneous information and/or describe information that is missing. II

Given a word phrase or sentence, express it as a mathematical phrase or sentence. Given a mathematical phrase or sentence, express it as a word phrase or sentence. II

Find the value of formulas using given values of the necessary variables. II

Find the solution set for a simple open sentence by substituting elements from a given replacement set. II

Write an open sentence for a given word problem that may contain extraneous information. Find the solution set by direct computation or by substitution (trial and error), or recognize the impossibility of finding a solution because of missing information. III

MA 425   Show that you can solve word problems relating to consumer needs. III

Given the hourly wage and the number of hours worked in a week, determine the weekly, monthly, and annual wages. III

Given the times in and out, the company's regular work hours, overtime, and any sick leave and annual leave taken, complete a time card for one week.   II

Given the number of pieces of work completed daily for a week and the rate per piece, determine the weekly wage.   III

Given a salary and the deductions, determine the amount of take-home pay.   III

Given an itemized list of expenditures and the annual income for a family, compute the percent of the income spent for each item.   III

Given the amount of annual income and the percent of the income to be spent on various items, compute the amount to be allocated to each item in a monthly budget.   III

Given the price of one unit, find the price of *n* units.   III

Given the price of *n* units, find the price of one unit.   III

Given the cost of a specific quantity of a product and the cost of a different quantity of the same product, determine the cost per unit for both quantities to learn which rate is cheaper.   III

Given a list of purchased items, the amount charged for each item, and the sales tax rate, demonstrate how a sales slip would show the price of each item, the tax, and the total bill.   III

Given the total bill and the amount of money paid to the cashier, determine the number and variety of bills and/or coins to be given in change.   III

Given the appropriate table of fares, determine the cost of traveling by plane, bus, ship, or train between any two cities.   III

Using a given map or chart, determine the distance between two given cities.   III

Given the average speed and the average gas mileage for a car, the cost of gas, and the distance between two given cities, deter-

INTERMEDIATE

mine the traveling time and cost of gas for a trip in this car between the two cities.   III

Using a given plane, ship, bus, or train schedule, determine the time needed to travel between two given cities on that mode of transportation.   III

Given the restrictions on size and weight of letters and packages, recognize whether a given letter or package can be mailed and give the reason.   II

Given a table of parcel post rates and information about the distance between cities, find the cost of mailing a given package from one city to any other city in the United States.   II

Given a table of rates for first-class mail, air mail, special delivery, and registered mail, determine the cost of mailing a given letter or package (1) first class, (2) air mail, (3) special delivery, or (4) registered mail.   III

Given a table of rates for freight, express, and air express, determine the cost of shipping a given package in one of these ways.   III

MA 430   Show that you can solve problems relating to consumer living.   III

Using a given scale, construct a scale drawing of a room showing doors, windows, and a furniture arrangement of your choice.   III

Given the measurements of a room, the size and number of windows and doors, the amount of paint needed to cover a given surface, and the cost of the paint, determine the cost of painting the room.   III

Given the measurements of the windows in a room, a description of the kind of curtain desired, and the cost of material per yard, determine the total cost of the material necessary for making the curtains.   III

Given a recipe for n people, determine the amount of ingredients for $<n$ people.   III

Given a recipe for *n* people, determine the amount of ingredients for >*n* people.   III

Given a recipe that serves *n* people and the cost of a given amount of each of the ingredients, determine the cost of serving one person.   III

Given a recipe that serves *n* people and the number of calories in a given amount of each of the ingredients, determine the number of calories in a serving for one person.   III

Given a scale drawing of an item to be constructed and the materials to be used, determine the amount of each material needed to build the item.   III

Given the measurements of an item, decrease or increase its measurements *n* times and determine its new measurements.   III

Given an itemized list of the amounts of various materials used in constructing an item and the cost per unit of each material, determine the total cost of the materials necessary to construct the item.   III

Given a schedule of rates for electricity and an electric bill (from which the number of kilowatt hours used can be determined), determine the total cost of the electricity used. Compare this cost with the amount shown on the electric bill.   III

Given a schedule of rates for gas and a gas bill (from which the number of cubic feet used can be determined), determine the total cost of the gas used. Compare this cost with the amount shown on the gas bill.   III

Given a schedule of rates for water and a water bill (from which the number of cubic feet used can be determined), determine the total cost of the water used. Compare this cost with the amount shown on the water bill.   III

Given a table of telephone rates, the type and number of calls made in a given month, and the telephone bill for the month (including federal and local taxes), determine whether the total shown on the telephone bill is correct.   III

INTERMEDIATE

Given a table of annual premiums for three types of life insurance coverage (straight life, limited life, and endowment), the amount and type of insurance purchased, and the age of the policyholder at the time of purchase, determine what percent of the total amount of the policy he will have paid in premiums in n years. III

Given a table of annual premiums for bodily injury, property damage, comprehensive damage, and collision insurance for different types of driving, determine the total annual premium for a car used for pleasure, for driving to work, or for business. III

Given the annual premium rates of coverage for fire insurance and the amount of coverage, determine the premium for one year. III

Given the original price of a car, its age, and its trade-in or resale value, determine the average annual depreciation of the car. III

Given the original cost and the average annual depreciation of a car, determine the rate of depreciation. III

Given the annual payments for taxes, insurance, gasoline, oil, repairs, interest, and depreciation, determine the total annual operating cost and the average monthly operating cost of a car. III

Given the readings of the odometer on two successive fillings of the gas tank and the amount of gasoline needed to fill the tank the second time, determine the gas mileage. III

Given any two of the following, determine the third: (1) distance traveled, (2) traveling time, (3) average speed in miles per hour. III

MA 435 Show that you can apply mathematical operations to problems dealing with sports. III

Given the number of errors made by a baseball player and the number of chances he had to make an error, determine the fielding percentage. III

Given the wins and losses for two baseball teams, determine how many games one team lags behind the other.   III

Given the number of runs scored against a baseball pitcher and the number of innings he pitches, determine his earned-run average.   III

Given the number of games won and the total number of games played for the baseball teams in a league, determine the standing of a given team.   III

Given the number of hits made by a baseball player and his times at bat, determine his batting average.   III

Given the number of yards gained by passing and the number of passes attempted in a football game, find the average number of yards gained by passing.   III

Given the number of passes thrown and the number of passes completed by a football player in a specified number of games, find the average percent of passes completed (passing average).   III

Given the total yards gained in rushing by a football team or player and the number of times the ball was carried, find the average number of yards gained in rushing.   III

Given the number of games played by a football team and the number of points for each game, find the average number of points made per game by the team.   III

Given the number of field goals and the number of free throws made in a basketball game by a player or a team, find the player's or team's total score.   III

Given the number of free throws made and the number of free throws attempted by a basketball player or team in a given game or season, find the percentage of free throws made.   III

Given the number of field goals, the number of free throws made, and the number of games for a basketball player or team, find the average number of points per game.   III

INTERMEDIATE

Given the number of field goals, the number of free throws made, and the time played by a basketball player, find his average scoring per minute played.   III

Given the number of games and the total number of rebounds made by a basketball player, find the average number of rebounds per game for the player.   III

Given the number of games and the total number of assists made by a basketball player, find the average number of assists per game for the player.   III

MA 440 **Show that you can apply mathematical operations to problems dealing with occupations and future education.   III**

Given the number of people in an occupation and the total working population, find the percent of the total working population in the given occupation.   III

Given the present population and the expected rate of population increase, predict what the population will be in *n* years. III

Given the percent of people in a given occupation and the predicted total working population in *n* years, predict the number of people in that occupation in *n* years.   III

Given the average yearly wage for an occupation and the average years of employment in that occupation, find the average total life income for a person in that occupation.   III

Given the cost of training and the total life income for an occupation, find what percent of life income the cost of training represents.   III

Given an itemized list of college expenditures — including tuition, room and board, books, travel expenses, and personal expenses — for one month or year, find the cost of attending college for four years.   III

Given the present average cost of attending college for one year and the predicted average rate of increase, predict the annual cost in *n* years.   III

Given the amount of a scholarship for one year and the total annual cost of college, find the percent of the total that is paid by the scholarship.   III

Given the total cost for one year of college, determine how much you would have to save yearly for any given number of years to pay for one year of college, without considering the interest you might earn.   III

SECONDARY

analysis of number and system

MA 500 **Show that you can use arithmetic operations on whole numbers, fractions, and decimals to solve given problems.   III**

Identify the place value for each place (digit) of any numeral with up to 9 digits.   I

Find the sum of two numbers.   II

Find the difference of two numbers.   II

Demonstrate that two numbers may be added in either order without changing the sum (order principle).   III

Demonstrate that when three or more numbers are added, they may be grouped in any way without changing the sum (grouping principle).   III

Multiply two numbers using the distributive property of multiplication over addition.   II

Multiply whole numbers where the factors have 1, 2, or 3 digits.   II

Multiply a 2- or 3-digit number by a multiple of 10.   II

Divide a 2- or 3-place number by a 1- or 2-place number.   II

Solve division problems involving 0.   II

Identify the numerator and denominator of a given fraction.   I

Express the proper fraction suggested by a picture.   II

Given a proper fraction, express equivalent fractions.   II

Express a proper fraction in lowest terms.   II

Express the improper fraction suggested by a picture. II

Add two proper fractions. II

Subtract one proper fraction from another. II

Rewrite an improper fraction as a whole number or as a mixed number. II

Rewrite a mixed number or a whole number as an improper fraction. II

Add two mixed numbers. II

Subtract one mixed number from another. II

Multiply a whole number by a proper fraction. II

Multiply two proper fractions. II

Multiply two mixed numbers. II

Given the product and one factor of a multiplication problem, find the missing factor. II

Divide one fraction by another fraction. II

Identify the place value for any given digit of a decimal fraction. I

Express a decimal fraction as a mixed number or as a common fraction with a denominator of 10, 100, or 1000. II

Express a fraction or a mixed number as a decimal fraction. II

Add decimal numbers. II

Subtract one decimal number from another decimal number. II

SECONDARY

Multiply a 1-, 2-, or 3-place decimal fraction by another 1-, 2-, or 3-place decimal fraction. II

Divide a decimal fraction by a whole number or by another decimal fraction. II

Given a slide rule, identify the following parts and their functions: (1) the rule proper, (2) the slide, (3) the runner, and (4) the scales. I

Use the slide rule to multiply 2-digit numbers. II

Use the slide rule to divide a 2-digit number by another 2-digit number. II

Use the slide rule to square any 2-digit number. II

Use the slide rule to find the square root of any number. II

MA 505   Show that you can solve problems requiring the use of properties of real numbers or of complex numbers. III

Express rational numbers as repeating or terminating decimals and vice versa. II

Find an irrational number between any two real numbers. II

Recognize examples of the following properties and, given an example, recognize the property: (1) closure properties of addition and multiplication, (2) commutative properties of addition and multiplication, and (3) associative properties of addition and multiplication. II

Recognize the distributive property and use it to combine like terms. II

Write formal proofs of real-number theorems using the properties of real numbers. III

Find decimal approximations for irrational numbers by graphing and by using tables. II

Considering the standard form $a + bi$ where a and b are real numbers, describe in writing the conditions for which two complex numbers are equal. II

Add, subtract, and multiply complex numbers of the form $a + bi$. II

Find the conjugates of complex numbers and use them in dividing complex numbers. II

Given complex numbers of the form $a + bi$, find the identity element and the additive inverse. Demonstrate with examples that the associative and commutative properties of addition and multiplication should hold for complex numbers of the form $a + bi$ and that the distributive property of multiplication over addition also holds. III

Determine whether the roots of the equation $ax^2 + bx + c = 0$ where a, b, and c are real numbers are complex by using the discriminant. If they are complex, determine the graph of the equation on the real plane. Solve equations with complex co-efficients. III

Find the sum and difference of complex numbers graphically. II

MA 510 **Show that you can solve problems requiring the use of properties of arithmetic, geometric and binomial expansions. III**

Derive the formula for the nth term of an arithmetic progression (AP). II

Find the nth term of a given arithmetic progression. II

Calculate and write the arithmetic mean between two terms of an arithmetic progression. II

Derive the formula for the sum of an arithmetic progression (a series) and find the sum for a given number of terms of an arithmetic series. II

Solve word problems using arithmetic progressions. III

SECONDARY

Derive the formula for the nth term of a geometric progression (GP) and find the nth term of a given geometric progression.   II

Find the geometric mean between two terms of a geometric progression.   II

Derive the formula for the sum of a geometric progression (a series) and find the sum for a given number of terms of a geometric series.   II

Derive the formula for an infinite geometric series and find the sum of an infinite geometric series.   II

Solve word problems using geometric series.   III

Solve problems using factorial notation.   II

Expand binomials such as $(a + b)^n$ where n is an integer less than 10.   II

Find any term of a binomial expansion using the binomial theorem.   II

Prove the binomial theorem by mathematical induction and use the results to solve related problems.   III

OPERATIONS: NUMERICAL AND ALGEBRAIC

MA 515   Show that you can solve simple linear equations.   III

Find the value of a given algebraic expression that represents one or more operations.   II

Using the trial and error method, solve an equation.   II

Using the method of applying the inverse operation, solve an equation involving one indicated operation.   II

Solve an equation that involves more than one indicated operation. II

Solve an equation that involves like terms. II

MA 520 Show that you can solve word problems by using algebraic equations. III

Solve word problems using addition or subtraction. III

Solve word problems using multiplication. III

Solve word problems using division. III

Solve word problems using addition and subtraction of fractions. III

Solve word problems using multiplication and/or division of fractions. III

Solve word problems using addition or subtraction of decimals. III

Solve a word problem using multiplication or division of decimal fractions. III

Express a common fraction or decimal fraction as a percent and write a percent as a decimal fraction or a common fraction. II

Solve word problems using percent. III

Translate words into algebraic expressions or sentences and translate algebraic expressions into words. II

Solve word problems with one unknown by writing and solving equations. II

Write an equation and solve it to find the missing term in a proportion or solve a problem that can be represented by a proportion. III

Use proportions to solve problems involving percents. II

SECONDARY

MA 525 **Show that you can perform basic algebraic operations and simplifications including factoring. III**

Add integers (directed numbers). II

Using the definition of subtraction, $a - b = a + (-b)$, find the difference of two integers. II

Multiply integers (directed numbers). II

Using the following definition, find the quotient of any two integers: "A rational number is one that can be expressed as the quotient of two integers $\left(\dfrac{a}{b}, b \neq 0\right)$." II

Add and subtract polynomials. II

Using the rules $a^n \cdot a^m = a^{m+n}$ and $(ab)^n = a^n b^n$, simplify algebraic expressions. II

Multiply polynomials by monomials. II

Using the distributive property, multiply polynomials by polynomials or expand powers of polynomials. II

Using the following law of exponents, divide a monomial by a monomial: $\dfrac{a^n}{a^m} = a^{n-m}$ where $n \geq m$ and n and m are whole numbers. II

Divide a polynomial by a polynomial. II

Find the greatest common monomial factor of a polynomial. II

Using the sentence $a^2 - b^2 = (a + b)(a - b)$, find the difference of two squares as a product of a sum and a difference and the product of a sum and a difference as the difference of two squares. II

Using the sentences $(a + b)^2 = a^2 + 2ab + b^2$ and $(a - b)^2 = a^2 - 2ab + b^2$, factor and expand binomials. II

Find the product of any two binomials mentally and factor any trinomial that is factorable over the integers. II

Completely factor trinomials. II

Define an algebraic fraction and recognize the restrictions placed on the variables in the denominator. II

Simplify (reduce) algebraic fractions. II

Find the product of two algebraic fractions. II

Find the quotient of two algebraic fractions. II

Find the sum and difference of two or more algebraic fractions. II

Given any two rational numbers in fractional form, find a rational number that is between them. II

Write common fractions as repeating decimals and repeating decimals as common fractions. II

Using the rules of radicals, simplify radicals and, using square root tables or approximation methods, find the square root of a given number. II

Simplify radicals that involve multiplication or division. II

Simplify radicals that involve addition or subtraction. II

Using the conjugate of a number, simplify expressions containing radicals. II

Using the fundamental order of operations, simplify numerical expressions. II

SECONDARY

MA 530 **Show that you can solve word problems by using algebraic techniques.** III

Write algebraic sentences or phrases from word problems. III

Solve word problems whose translations involve equations similar to $x + a = b$ or $ax + b = c$. III

Write simple equations for given word problems and solve them. III

Solve word problems that require the solution of an inequality. III

Solve word problems that involve multiplication of polynomials. III

Solve word problems that involve factorable quadratic equations. III

Solve word problems that involve fractional equations. III

Solve word problems that involve systems of two simultaneous linear equations. III

Solve word problems that can be solved by using the Pythagorean Theorem. III

Solve direct variation problems (special type of functions). II

Solve inverse variation problems. II

Solve word problems that can be solved by using the quadratic formula. III

MA 535 **Show that you can solve equations and inequalities including linear and quadratic systems and polynomial equations.** III

Rewrite verbal descriptions of sets into set notation and, given a set in set notation, give its verbal description. II

Recognize subsets of infinite sets and subsets of finite sets.   II

Solve algebraic expressions for various values of the variable.   II

Given a replacement set for a variable, find the truth set of an open sentence by substitution.   II

Use the following property to solve equations: If a, b, and c are numbers of arithmetic and $a = b$, then $a + c = b + c$ and $a - c = b - c$.   II

Use the following property to solve equations: If a, b, and c ($c \neq 0$) are numbers of arithmetic and $a = b$, then $ac = bc$ and $\frac{a}{c} = \frac{b}{c}$.   II

Solve equations that require more than one step for the solution.   II

Solve equations that contain rational numbers.   II

Given the follow properties, use them to recognize relationships about numbers.   II
1. If $a < b$, then $a + c = b$ for some $c > 0$.
2. If $a < b$, then $a + c < b + c$ for all c.
3. If $a < b$, then $\frac{a}{c} < \frac{b}{c}$ if $c > 0$.
4. If $a < b$, $b < c$, then $a < c$.

Solve simple inequalities and graph the solutions.   II

Solve compound inequalities and graph the solution sets.   II

Using the theorem $ab = 0$ if and only if $a = 0$ or $b = 0$, solve equations that are factorable.   II

Solve fractional equations.   II

Using the addition or subtraction method, solve a system of two simultaneous linear equations.   II

SECONDARY

Solve equations that contain radicals.   II

Solve quadratic equations that can be written in the form $(x - a)^2 = b^2$ where a and b are real numbers.   II

If the roots of $ax^2 + bx + c = 0$ are r_1 and r_2 find the relationships between the coefficients a, b, and c and r_1 and r_2.   II

Solve quadratic equations by completing the square.   II

Given $ax^2 + bx + c = 0$, find a formula (quadratic formula) for x where x is a real number.   II

Find the discriminant of a quadratic equation and use it to determine the nature of the roots.   III

MA 540   Show that you can perform complex algebraic operations and simplifications.   III

Simplify numerical expressions involving the four basic operations on real numbers.   II

Simplify polynomials by using the basic laws of positive integral exponents.   II

Multiply polynomials over the real numbers.   II

Factor these special expressions: (1) $a^2 - b^2$, (2) $a^2 + 2ab + b^2$, (3) $a^2 - 2ab + b^2$, (4) $a^3 + b^3$, (5) $a^3 - b^3$.   II

Given two different polynomials, express their greatest common factor (GCF) and their least common multiple (LCM) by using the prime factorization method.   II

Factor quadratic trinomials over the real numbers.   II

Simplify expressions with nonpositive integral exponents.   II

Rewrite expressions as rational algebraic expressions with the correct restrictions on the variables.   II

Use the multiplication property of 1 to simplify rational algebraic expressions.   II

Multiply and divide algebraic expressions.   II

Find the sum and difference of algebraic expressions.   II

Simplify complex fractions.   II

Simplify radicals using the theorems about products, quotients, and powers of radicals.   II

Simplify sums of radicals and products of sums containing radicals.   II

MA 545   Show that you can find the derivative of an algebraic, trigonometric, inverse trigonometric, exponential, or logarithmic function.   III

Solve quadratic equations and quadratic inequations (inequalities) by factoring or graphing.   II

Determine and solve quadratic equations that are derived from word problems.   III

Solve fractional equations and fractional inequations (inequalities).   II

Solve word problems that involve fractional equations.   III

Solve equations and inequalities that may or may not contain absolute values, and solve open sentences that are derived from word problems.   III

Solve first degree systems of n equations in n unknowns for $n \leqslant 4$.   II

Solve linear systems derived from word problems.   III

Use the numerical coefficients of an equation with integral coefficients to find all of the possible rational roots.   II

Solve quadratic equations by completing the square and by using the quadratic formula.   II

Given any quadratic equation with real coefficients and using the relations between roots and coefficients and the discriminant, find (1) the nature of the roots, (2) the sum of the roots, and (3) the product of the roots.   II

Solve quadratic inequalities and equations containing radicals.   II

Solve equations involving inverse variation.   II

Solve linear-quadratic systems by the algebraic method.   II

Solve quadratic-quadratic systems.   II

Given a specific point, find the value of a polynomial function by synthetic substitution.   II

Using the factor theorem and/or remainder theorem, find factors or remainders or roots that are associated with a given polynomial.   II

Find the roots of a polynomial equation with real coefficients, using Descartes' Rule of Signs and this theorem: "If a polynomial equation with real coefficients has $a + bi$ as a root (a and b real, $b \neq 0$), then $a - bi$ is also a root."   II

Graph a polynomial function through the use of (1) synthetic substitution, (2) a table of values, (3) the property of continuity, and (4) the change of signs.   II

Find the integral lower and upper bounds for the roots of polynomial equations.   II

1A 550   Show that you can apply knowledge of the properties and functions and limits without reference to calculus.   III

Define and use the following terms and notations: *relation, function, mapping, image,* $f(x)$, $f{:}x \rightarrow f(x)$, *domain,* and *range.*   II

MATHEMATICS

Given a relation, determine whether the graph describes a function. Solve problems related to the graphs of step functions and absolute value functions.   III

Given a relation or function, determine if its inverse exists, write or graph the inverse and solve related problems.   III

Given two or three rational functions, determine a particular composite function and solve related problems.   III

Apply theorems about inverse functions to solve problems.   I

Define the functions $y = \ln x$ and $y = e^x$ as inverse functions and determine their properties.   III

Using the properties of limits listed below, find limits where $F(t)$ and $G(t)$ are polynomials.   II

1. $\lim\limits_{t \to a}[F(t) + G(t)] = \lim\limits_{t \to a} F(t) + \lim G(t)$

2. $\lim\limits_{t \to a}[kF(t)] = k \lim\limits_{t \to a} F(t)$

3. $\lim\limits_{t \to a}[F(t) \cdot G(t)] = \lim\limits_{t \to a} F(t) \cdot \lim\limits_{t \to a} G(t)$

4. $\lim\limits_{t \to a}\dfrac{F(t)}{G(t)} = \dfrac{\lim\limits_{t \to a} F(t)}{\lim\limits_{t \to a} G(t)}, \lim\limits_{t \to a} G(t) \neq 0$

Using the concept of a limit, find the slope of a given polynomial function at a given point.   II

Using the definition of continuity, test a given function for continuity at a given point.   II

MA 555 **Show that you can apply methods of calculus or numerical analysis to the approximation of functional values, transcendental functions, and definite integrals.   III**

Demonstrate an understanding of differentials by interpreting them geometrically and by relating them to $\triangle x$ and $\triangle y$.

Given an algebraic function, estimate the functional value for given values of x and $\triangle x$, using $\triangle y \approx \dfrac{dy}{dx} \triangle x$.   II

SECONDARY

Using differentials, determine approximations to radicals and powers. III

Using Newton's method, approximate the roots of a given algebraic equation. III

Given a definite integral of a simple algebraic function, use the trapezoidal rule to determine an approximate numerical value. III

Using Simpson's rule, determine an approximate numerical value of a given definite integral of an algebraic or a transcendental function. III

Determine a polynomial function of degree n (where $n \leqslant 4$) whose graph passes through a given set of points. III

Using polynomials, determine to a preassigned accuracy an approximate value of e^x for a given value of x near 0 or an approximate value of $\ln x$ for a given value of x near 1. III

Using polynomials, determine to a preassigned accuracy an approximate value of $\sin x$ or of $\cos x$ for a given value of x. III

OPERATIONS: GRAPHICS

MA 560 **Show that you can apply the definitions, relationships, and theorems of numerical trigonometry to the solution of problems. III**

On the coordinate plane, recognize angles in standard position and solve related problems. II

From sets of ordered pairs of real numbers or from linear functions that determine the terminal side of an angle θ, find the value of the sine of $\theta(\sin \theta)$ and of the cosine of $\theta(\cos \theta)$. II

Define the tangent, cotangent, secant, and cosecant functions. Given one of the trigonometric ratios for any angle θ, find the values of the remaining trigonometric functions. II

Find the values of the functions of quadrantal angles and th special angles (30°, 45°, 60°). II

Apply the values of the functions of quadrantal angles and th special angles (30°, 45°, 60°) to relate trigonometric function and their cofunctions. III

Determine reference angles for any angle θ in standard positio and solve corresponding function value problems. III

Use a table of values of trigonometric functions to find (1) th value of trigonometric functions, and (2) angles from a give numerical value of a trigonometric function of some angle.

Use logarithms of the values of trigonometric functions to solv problems involving operations with trigonometric functions.

Solve word problems that require construction of right triangle and computations with trigonometric functions. III

Use the distance formula to derive the Law of Cosines ($c^2 = a^2$ $b^2 - 2ab$, cos C), and apply the Law of Cosines in solving prob lems. III

Given two sides and the included angle of a triangle, derive th formula for its area. II

Given two sides and the included angle of a triangle, find th area of a triangle. II

Derive the Law of Sines, $\dfrac{\sin A}{a} = \dfrac{\sin B}{b} = \dfrac{\sin C}{c}$. Use this law t solve related problems. II

Given the measurements for two sides and one angle (not th included angle) of a triangle, find all the triangles having thos measurements. II

Given the measures of some of the sides and/or angles of a tr angle, find the measures of the remaining sides and/or angles.

Solve word problems that require the use of trigonometric functions. Construct meaningful diagrams as an aid in solving these problems.   III

MA 565   Show that you can find the derivative of an algebraic, trigonometric, inverse trigonometric, exponential, or logarithmic function.   III

Define the derivative of a function and identify common notations for it.   II

Using the definition of derivative, find the derivative, if it exists, of a given rational function.   II

Using the definition of derivative, develop formulas for differentiating the following types of functions.   V
1. $y = x^n$ where n is a positive integer.
2. $y = cu$ where c is a constant and u is a differentiable function.
3. $y = u + v$ where u and v are differentiable functions.
4. $y = u \cdot v$ where u and v are differentiable functions.

5. $y = \dfrac{u}{v}$ where u and v are differentiable functions.

Using the appropriate formula, determine the derivative of given functions of the following types: III
1. $y = u + v$ where u and v are differentiable functions
2. $y = u \cdot v$ where u and v are differentiable functions

3. $y = \dfrac{u}{v}$ where u and v are differentiable functions

Use the chain rule to determine the derivative of a composite function.   III

Differentiate a given function defined implicitly.   III

Given an incomplete proof of the derivation of the formula for $\dfrac{d}{du}$ (sin u), find the missing details.   II

Given a composite trigonometric function (sine, cosine, or tangent), find its derivative.   II

MATHEMATICS

Given an inverse trigonometric function (arc sin, arc cos, or arc tan), find its derivative. II

Determine $\dfrac{dy}{dx}$ or $\dfrac{d^2y}{dx^2}$ where x and y are expressed parametrically as functions of a third variable. III

Find the derivative of a function of the form $y = \ln u$ where u is a differentiable function of x. II

Find the derivative of a function of the form $y = e^u$ where u is a differentiable function of x. II

Use logarithmic differentiation to find the derivative of a function of the form $y = v^u$ where u and v are both differentiable function of x. II

Find the derivative of a function of the form $y = a^u$ where u is a differentiable function of x. II

MA 570   **Show that you can derive and use the multiple-angle formula to prove that an equation is an identity and to solve an equation. III**

Prove that a given equation is a trigonometric identity by use of the reciprocal, quotient, and Pythagorean Relation. III

Given two points in the plane, P and Q, with p and q being the distance from the origin to those points with respective position angles α and β, and using $x = p \cos \theta$ and $y = p \sin \theta$ and the rectangular coordinate distance formula, derive the distance formula $(PQ)^2 = p^2 + q^2 - 2pq (\cos \alpha \cos \beta + \sin \alpha \sin \beta)$. Use the distance formula to solve problems. II

Derive the formula for the cosine of the difference of two angles and solve related problems. II

Given $\cos (\alpha - \beta) = \cos \alpha \cos \beta + \sin \alpha \sin \beta$, derive the following formulas. II
1. $\cos (\alpha + \beta) = \cos \alpha \cos \beta - \sin \alpha \sin \beta$
2. $\sin (\alpha + \beta) = \sin \alpha \cos \beta + \cos \alpha \sin \beta$
3. $\sin (\alpha - \beta) = \sin^\circ\alpha \cos \beta - \cos \alpha \sin \beta$

4. $\tan (\alpha + \beta) = \dfrac{\tan \alpha + \tan \beta}{1 - \tan \alpha \tan \beta}$

5. $\tan (\alpha - \beta) = \dfrac{\tan \alpha - \tan \beta}{1 + \tan \alpha \tan \beta}$

From the sum and difference formulas, derive and use the double and half-angle formulas.   II

1. $\sin 2B = 2 \sin B \cos B$ 4. $\sin \dfrac{\theta}{2} = \sqrt{\dfrac{1 - \cos \theta}{2}}$

2. $\cos 2B = \cos^2 B - \sin^2 B$ 5. $\cos \dfrac{\theta}{2} = \sqrt{\dfrac{1 + \cos \theta}{2}}$

3. $\tan 2B = \dfrac{2 \tan B}{1 - \tan^2 B}$ 6. $\tan \dfrac{\theta}{2} = \dfrac{1 - \cos \theta}{1 + \cos \theta}$

From the sum and difference formulas, derive and use the sum and product formulas.   II
1. $2 \sin \alpha \cos \beta = \sin (\alpha + \beta) + \sin (\alpha - \beta)$
2. $2 \cos \alpha \cos \beta = \cos (\alpha + \beta) + \cos (\alpha - \beta)$
3. $-2 \sin \alpha \sin \beta = \cos (\alpha + \beta) - \cos (\alpha - \beta)$

4. $\sin A + \sin B = 2 \sin \dfrac{A + B}{2} \cos \dfrac{A - B}{2}$

5. $\sin A - \sin B = 2 \cos \dfrac{A + B}{2} \sin \dfrac{A - B}{2}$

6. $\cos A + \cos B = 2 \cos \dfrac{A + B}{2} \cos \dfrac{A - B}{2}$

7. $\cos A - \cos B = -2 \sin \dfrac{A + B}{2} \sin \dfrac{A - B}{2}$

Solve open sentences that may require a substitution of any of the trigonometric identities.   III

MA 575   **Show that you can use the definitions of the circular functions and their inverses to graph and to solve analytic problems.   III**

Convert degree measurements to radian measurements or vice versa and solve related problems.   II

Define the circular functions and solve related problems.   II

Graph the functions $y = \sin x$, $y = \cos x$, and $y = \tan x$ on the real number plane.   II

Graph on the real number plane functions of the forms $y = a \sin bx$, $y = a \cos bx$, and $y = a \tan bx$.   II

Define arc cos $\frac{1}{2}$, inverse sin $\frac{1}{2}$, $\tan^{-1} \frac{1}{2}$, and solve related problems.   II

Define and graph the inverse circular functions of arc cos x, arc sin x, and arc tan x, and solve related problems.   II

Solve for general and particular solutions of open sentences that may require a substitution of the reciprocal, quotient, and Pythagorean identities.   II

Solve open sentences that may require a substitution of any of the trigonometric identities.   II

MA 580   **Show that you can graph plane curves specified in rectangular or polar coordinates, including those given by parametric equations.   III**

Use each of the following to graph curves: (1) symmetry, (2) tangents to a curve at the origin, (3) horizontal and vertical asymptotes, (4) empty bands, and (5) intercepts.   II

Graph compound curves by the addition of ordinates or product of ordinates methods.   II

Recognize and graph curves given by parametric equations and be able to eliminate the parameter.   II

Recognize and graph special curves given in parametric form (e.g., cycloid, hypocycloid, epicycloid).   II

Given an equation in rectangular coordinates, find an equivalent polar equation. Given a polar equation, find an equivalent rectangular equation.   II

Solve problems related to the polar form of lines and circles and rotate polar curves that contain only cosine of 90°, 180°, or 270°. III

SECONDARY

Recognize the polar form of the parabola, the ellipse, and the hyperbola, and draw them.   II

Graph polar curves using each of the following: (1) symmetry, (2) tangents at the origin, (3) possible values of r, (4) charts of polar curves, and (5) rotation theorem.   III

MA 585   Show that you can graph truth sets of quadratic equations and inequalities and that you can graph functions and relations.   III

Graph a set of numbers on a number line.   II

Given the replacement set for the variable in an open sentence, graph the truth set.   II

Graph truth sets of open sentences including sentences that have absolute value.   II

Given a linear equation in two variables, construct its graph.   II

Given any two points on a nonvertical line, write the equation of the line and find its slope.   III

Given an inequality with linear terms, construct its graph.   II

Graph systems of inequalities in two variables.   II

Graph relations and write equations for relations.   III

Recognize functions and graph functions.   II

Graph the truth set of quadratic inequalities.   II

MA 590   Show that you can find the integral of an algebraic or transcendental function by using a basic integration formula or a standard technique of integration.   III

Using basic integration formulas, evaluate directly given integrals of the type $\int u^n du$, where n is an algebraic or transcendental function and u is any number.   III

Integrate a given trigonometric function that requires the substitution of a trigonometric identity.   II

Using a trigonometric substitution, integrate a given algebraic function that involves the sum or difference of two squares.   II

Using the method of partial fractions, integrate a given rational function.   II

Integrate a given function by parts.   II

MA 595   **Show that you can graph relations and functions and find equations of relations and functions, both linear and quadratic.   III**

Graph a relation on the coordinate plane that is defined by a set of ordered pairs or an open sentence.   II

Graph equations of straight lines.   II

Given two points that lie on a line or one point and the slope, find the equation of the line.   II

Graph quadratic inequalities.   II

Use the distance formula to find the distance between any two points in the plane.   II

Given the center and the radius of a circle, express the equation of the circle and graph it.   II

Given an equation of a circle in the form $ax^2 + ay^2 + bx + cy + F = 0$, express the equation in the form $(x - h)^2 + (y - k)^2 = r^2$ (center-radius form).   II

Given the directrix, the focus, and the definition of a parabola, find the equation of the parabola.   II

Given the foci and definition of ellipse, find its equation.   II

Find the equation of a hyperbola from its definitions and graph it.   II

SECONDARY

Graph the equation for an equilateral hyperbola that is also an inverse variation. II

Graph systems of equations with at least one quadratic equation. II

MA 600 **Show that you can solve problems requiring the use of properties of exponential, logarithmic, linear, and quadratic functions. III**

Using special notation such as $f(x)$, solve problems involving functions. II

Solve direct variation problems using facts about linear functions. II

Given an equation of a line, the graph of a line, or any two points of a line, find the slope. II

Solve problems involving quadratic functions specified by the equation $y = az^2$. II

Find the vertex and axis of symmetry for any quadratic function specified by $y = a(x - h)^2 + k$. II

Find the vertex, indicating whether it is maximum or minimum, and the axis of symmetry of any quadratic function specified by $y = ax^2 + bx + c$. II

Given numbers in their exponential form, express them in their logarithmic form. Solve equations and simplify algebraic expressions that contain logarithms. II

Find logarithms and antilogarithms of numbers using tables and linear interpolation. II

Using theorems for logarithms of products and quotients, multiply and divide numbers and solve equations. II

Apply logarithms in evaluating exponential expressions, computing answers to word problems, and solving equations. III

Use the formula $Log_b N = \dfrac{Log_c N}{Log_c b}$ to solve exponential equations. II

Identify the conditions for which two lines are perpendicular. I

Geometry

MA 605   **Using formulas, solve word problems that require finding the perimeters, areas, and volumes of geometric shapes.   III**

Using formulas, find the perimeters of triangles, squares, rectangles, parallelograms, trapezoids, other polygons, and circles. II

Using formulas, find the areas of rectangles, squares, parallelograms, triangles, trapezoids, and circles.   II

Using formulas, find the volumes of rectangular solids, cylinders, pyramids, cones, and spheres.   II

MA 610   **Show that you can construct geometric figures using a compass and unmarked straightedge.   III**

Use a protractor and a straightedge to construct to the nearest degree acute, right, obtuse, straight, or reflex angles (to 359°) and draw adjacent, vertical, complementary, or supplementary angle pairs of specified sizes.   II

Use a compass and an unmarked straightedge to construct a duplicate of a given angle of less than 360° and to construct the bisector of a given angle of less than 360°.   III

Use a compass and an unmarked straightedge to construct a line parallel to a given line through a given point not on the line.   III

Use a compass and an unmarked straightedge to construct the perpendicular to a line segment at a given point on the line segment and to construct the perpendicular bisector of a line segment.   III

Use a compass and an unmarked straightedge to construct the perpendicular to a line segment from a given point not on the line segment.   III

Use a compass and an unmarked straightedge to divide a line segment into a specified number of parts of equal length.   III

Use a compass and an unmarked straightedge to construct a triangle, given the length of each side, and to construct the duplicate of a given triangle.   III

Use a compass and an unmarked straightedge to construct a square, given the length of each side, and to construct the duplicate of a given quadrilateral.   III

Use a compass and an unmarked straightedge to construct a circle, given the length of the radius, and to construct a circle through three given points (not all on the same line).   III

Use a compass and an unmarked straightedge to construct the tangent to a circle at a given point on the circle.   III

Use a compass to duplicate the angles to demonstrate that each of the following is true for a given case.   III
1. The sum of the measures of the angles of any triangle is 180°.
2. The sum of the measures of the angles of any parallelogram is 360°.
3. If two parallel lines are cut by a transversal, the sum of two interior angles on the same side of the transversal is 180°.

Using the statement that "if two lines are cut by a transversal so that the sum of two interior angles on the same side of the transversal is 180°, then the lines are parallel" and using a compass to duplicate angles and to compare lengths of line segments, demonstrate that each of the following is true for a given case.   III
1. The line segment joining the midpoints of two sides of a triangle is parallel to the third side and measures half its length.
2. The line segments joining the consecutive midpoints of the sides of any quadrilateral form a parallelogram.

Solve word problems involving the measurement, construction, and addition of angles.   III

Define and construct the angle bisectors, medians, and altitudes of a triangle.   III

Given three sides, construct a triangle. Given two sides and the included angle, construct a triangle. Given two angles and the included side, construct a triangle.   III

Construct a perpendicular to a line (1) through a point on the line, (2) through the midpoint of the line, and (3) through a point not on the line.   III

Through a given point, construct a line parallel to a given line and divide a given line segment into any number of congruent parts.   III

Construct quadrilaterals when given various dimensions.   III

Construct a circle through any three noncollinear points. Find the center of any given circle.   III

Given an arc of a circle, construct the bisector of the arc and find the center of the circle.   III

Construct an inscribed circle within a given triangle.   III

Construct the tangent to a given circle at a given point on the circle.   III

Construct the tangents to a given circle from a given external point.   III

MA 615   Show that you can apply the Pythagorean Theorem, the concept of similar triangles, or trigonometric ratios to make indirect measurements.   II

Use proportions to find unknown lengths of sides in similar triangles.   II

Use the Pythagorean Theorem and a table of square roots to find the length of one of the sides of a right triangle.   II

SECONDARY

Solve word problems involving indirect measurement by using similar triangles or the Pythagorean Theorem. III

Apply the concept of similar triangles or the Pythagorean Theorem to make indirect measurements of distances outside the classroom. III

Express the sine, the cosine, or the tangent ratio for either acute angle of the right triangle. II

Using a table, find the value of the sine, of the cosine, or of the tangent for a given acute angle. II

Using a table, find the angle that corresponds to the given value of a sine, of a cosine, or of a tangent. II

Given the measure of one acute angle and of one side in a right triangle, use a trigonometric ratio of either acute angle to find the length of another side. II

Given the measure of two sides of a right triangle, use a trigonometric ratio to find the measure of one of the acute angles. II

Solve word problems involving indirect measurement by using trigonometric ratios. III

Apply the concept of trigonometric ratios to make indirect measurements of distances and angles outside the classroom. III

MA 620 **Show that you can construct deductive and indirect proofs and proofs using coordinate geometry. III**

Given arguments illustrating inductive and deductive reasoning, classify each as inductive or deductive. II

Recognize definitions of the following words: *theorem, definition, postulate, axiom, assumption, proof, direct proof, indirect proof.* II

Apply the definitions of *linear pair, supplementary, complementary, right angle, vertical angle,* and *adjacent angle* to prove congruence of angle theorems. III

Apply the basic congruence, or side-angle-side (SAS) postulate, in formal proofs. III

Apply the angle-side-angle (ASA) theorem in formal proofs. III

Using SAS and/or ASA, prove that two sides of a triangle are congruent if and only if the angles opposite these sides are congruent (isosceles triangle theorem). III

Apply the theorem that an exterior angle of a triangle is greater than either remote interior angle to prove theorems and solve problems. III

Prove and apply the side-angle-angle (SAA) theorem and the congruence theorems for right triangles (hypotenuse-angle, hypotenuse-leg, leg-leg). III

Prove theorems and solve word problems using the theorem of inequality of sides and angles within a triangle. III

Use the triangle-inequality theorem (sides) to solve related word problems and to write proofs. III

In solving problems and writing proofs, apply the theorem that in a given plane, through a given point of a given line or through a given external point, there is one and only one line (plane) perpendicular (⊥) to a given line. III

Prove and apply to problem situations the theorem that the perpendicular bisector of a segment, in a plane, is the set of all points of a plane that are equidistant from the endpoints of the segment. III

In solving problems and writing proofs, apply the theorem that if a line is perpendicular to each of two intersecting lines at their point of intersection, then it is perpendicular to the plane that contains them. III

Prove that the shortest segment to a plane from an external point is the perpendicular segment between them. (Use indirect proof.) III

SECONDARY

In writing proofs, apply the relationships between parallel lines and a transversal.   III

Prove that the sum of the measures of the angles in a triangle is 180° and apply related theorems to solving problems.   III

Use the relationship of the sides in a 30-60-90 triangle to solve word problems and write proofs.   III

In writing proofs, apply the theorem that if three or more parallel lines intercept congruent segments on one transversal, then they intercept congruent segments on any transversal.   III

Prove and apply theorems concerning diagonals, opposite sides, opposite angles, and consecutive angles of parallelograms.   III

Prove and apply theorems concerning diagonals, opposite sides, and opposite angles of quadrilaterals (sufficient conditions for a parallelogram).   III

Prove and apply theorems dealing with the angles and diagonals of a rhombus, a rectangle, and a square.   III

Prove and apply the theorem concerning the relationship between the segment connecting the midpoints of two sides of a triangle and the third side.   III

Prove the following theorem and answer related questions: "If two parallel planes are intersected by another plane, the lines of intersection are parallel."   III

Apply the properties of parallelism and perpendicularity of lines and planes to solving problems and writing proofs.   III

Prove and apply theorems concerning the areas of rectangles and triangles in writing proofs and solving problems.   III

Prove and apply theorems concerning the areas of trapezoids and parallelograms to write related proofs and solve problems.   III

Given that a line intersects two sides of a triangle and is parallel to the third side, prove theorems that are direct consequences of this fact and apply the theorems in solving problems. III

Solve word problems and write proofs using the theorem that if three angles of one triangle are congruent to three angles of a second triangle, then the triangles are similar. III

Given the following two theorems, prove theorems that are dependent on these two and apply them in solving problems. III
1. Two triangles are similar if two sides of one are proportional to two corresponding sides of the other and if the included angles are congruent.
2. Two triangles are similar if the three sides of one are proportional to the three sides of the other.

Solve word problems and write proofs applying theorems that deal with similarity between right triangles. III

Prove the theorem that a line tangent to a circle (sphere) is perpendicular to the radius at the point of contact. Apply this fact in solving problems and writing proofs. III

Prove that if a diameter is perpendicular to a chord, it bisects the chord. Apply this theorem to solve related problems and write proofs. III

Prove that congruent chords in the same circle or in congruent circles are equidistant from the center of the circle (sphere) and apply it in solving related problems and writing related proofs. III

Prove theorems and apply them in solving problems concerning the relationship between central angles and intercepted arcs. III

Prove that the measure of an inscribed angle is half the measure of its intercepted arc and apply this theorem in writing proofs and solving problems. III

Prove theorems concerning the angles formed by tangents, secants, and chords and apply them to related problems and proofs. III

SECONDARY

Prove theorems related to the lengths of segments formed by secants and tangents and apply them to related problems and proofs. III

Given a theorem to prove by coordinate geometry methods, apply the most appropriate coordinates to make the algebraic calculations as easy as possible. III

Given a theorem to prove by coordinate geometry methods, apply the most appropriate coordinates to insure that the proof is a general case, not a special case. III

Given a geometry theorem, prove the theorem by applying co-ordinate geometry definitions, theorems, and techniques. III

MA 625 Apply definitions and properties of angles and triangles to the solution of problems. III

Recognize the interior, exterior, and vertices of angles and of triangles and recognize different types of triangles. II

Solve word problems involving the measurement, construction, and addition of angles. III

Apply definitions of *linear pair, supplementary, complementary, right angle, vertical angle,* and *adjacent angle.* Prove congruence of angle theorems. III

Apply the basic congruence, or side-angle-side (SAS) postulate, in formal proofs. III

Apply the angle-side-angle (ASA) theorem in formal proofs. III

Using SAS and/or ASA, prove that two sides of a triangle are congruent if and only if the angles opposite these sides are congruent (isoceles-triangle theorem). III

Apply the side-side-side (SSS) theorem in formal proofs. III

Apply the theorem that an exterior angle of a triangle is greater than either remote interior angle to prove theorems and solve problems. III

Prove and apply the side-angle-angle theorem (SAA) and the congruence theorems for right triangles (hypotenuse-angle, hypotenuse-leg, leg-leg). III

Prove theorems and solve word problems using the theorem of inequality of sides and angles within a triangle. III

Use the triangle inequality theorem (sides) to solve related word problems and to write proofs. III

Apply the following theorem to problem situations: "If two sides of one triangle are $\cong$ respectively to two sides of a second $\triangle$ and the included angle of the first $\triangle$ is larger than the included angle of the second $\triangle$, then the third side of the first triangle is larger than the third side of the second." III

State and apply the Pythagorean Theorem in proofs and problem situations. III

Solve word problems requiring a discrimination between the definitions of *proportion, ratio, geometric mean* (mean proportion), and *similarity* ($\sim$). III

Given that a line intersects two sides of a triangle and is parallel to the third side, prove theorems that are direct consequences of this fact and apply the theorems in solving problems. III

Solve word problems and write proofs using the theorem that if three angles of one triangle are congruent to three angles of a second triangle, then the triangles are similar. III

Given the following two theorems, prove theorems that are dependent on these two and apply them in solving problems. III
1. Two triangles are similar if two sides of one are proportional to two corresponding sides of the other and if the included angles are congruent.
2. Two triangles are similar if the three sides of one are proportional to the three sides of the other.

Solve word problems and write proofs applying theorems dealing with similarity between right triangles. III

Find the ratio of the areas of similar triangles when given the dimensions of any corresponding parts. II

SECONDARY

MA 630 **Apply definitions and properties of lines and planes to the solution of problems. III**

Recognize definitions of the following words: *intersection, union, collinear, coplanar.* II

Using absolute value, find the distance between any two points on a line. II

Identify conditions that determine a line. (Line postulate: For every two points there is exactly one line that contains both points.) I

Identify symbols and definitions for *line, segment, ray, opposite rays, midpoint, endpoint, length, angle, triangle,* and *space.* I

Apply the definition of *congruence* ($\cong$) to line segments, angles, and polygons to solving problems. III

Identify all conditions that determine a plane. I

Describe the separation of a line by a point, a plane by a line, and a space by a plane in terms of convex sets. II

Apply to solving problems and writing proofs the theorem that in a given plane, through a given point of a given line or through a given external point, there is one and only one line (plane) perpendicular ($\perp$) to a given line. III

Prove and apply to problem situations the theorem that the perpendicular bisector of a segment, in a plane, is the set of all points of a plane that are equidistant from the endpoints of the segment. III

Apply to solving problems and writing proofs the theorem that if a line is perpendicular to each of two intersecting lines at their point of intersection, then it is perpendicular to the plane that contains them. III

Prove that the shortest segment to a plane from an external point is the perpendicular segment between them. Use indirect proof. III

Define and recognize parallel lines, skew lines, transversal, alternate interior angles, and corresponding angles.   II

Apply the relationships between parallel lines and a transversal to writing proofs.   III

Prove that the sum of the measures of the angles in a triangle is 180° and apply related theorems to solving problems.   III

Use the relationship of the sides in a 30-60-90 triangle to solve word problems and write proofs.   III

In writing proofs, apply the theorem that if three or more parallel lines intercept congruent segments on one transversal, then they intercept congruent segments on any transversal.   III

Prove the following theorem and answer related questions: "If two parallel planes are intersected by another plane, the lines of intersection are parallel."   III

Apply the properties of parallelism and perpendicularity of lines and planes to solving problems and writing proofs.   III

Define *dihedral angle, plane angle, measure of a dihedral angle, right dihedral angle,* and *perpendicularity of planes.*   II

Apply the congruence of plane angles of a dihedral-angle theorem and the perpendicularity-of-planes theorem to solving problems and writing proofs.   III

After defining the term *projection,* solve word problems related to finding the projection of a set of points.   III

MA 635   Apply definitions and properties of quadrilaterals and other polygons to the solution of problems.   III

Recognize and define *quadrilateral, convex quadrilateral, consecutive angles, opposite angles, diagonal, vertices, base, altitude, trapezoid, parallelogram, rectangle, square,* and *rhombus.*   II

SECONDARY

Prove and apply theorems concerning diagonals, opposite sides, opposite angles, and consecutive angles of parallelograms. III

Prove and apply theorems concerning diagonals, opposite sides, and opposite angles of quadrilaterals (sufficient conditions for a parallelogram). III

Prove and apply theorems dealing with the angles and diagonals of a rhombus, a rectangle, and a square. III

Prove and apply the theorem concerning the relationship between the segment connecting the midpoints of two sides of a triangle and the third side. III

Apply the area, congruence, area addition, and unit (square) postulates for polygons in solving problems. III

Prove and apply theorems concerning the areas of rectangles and triangles in writing proofs and solving problems. III

Prove and apply theorems concerning the areas of trapezoids and parallelograms to write related proofs and solve problems. III

Define the following terms as they apply to polygons: *vertices, sides, angles, diagonals, perimeter, apothem*. Name given polygons and classify them as regular or irregular, convex or not convex. II

Find the number of diagonals in a polygon of *n* sides using the formula $D = \frac{n}{2}(n - 3)$ and find the sum of the measures of the angles of a polygon of *n* sides using the formula $S_n = (n - 2)180$. II

MA 640 Show that you can apply definitions and properties of circles to the solution of problems. III

Define and solve problems concerning the common properties of circles and spheres in relation to center, radius, diameter, great circle, chord, secant, tangent, interior, and exterior. II

Prove the theorem that a line tangent to a circle (sphere) is perpendicular to the radius at the point of contact. Apply this fact in solving problems and writing proofs.   III

Prove that if a diameter is perpendicular to a chord, it bisects the chord. Apply this theorem to solve related problems and write proofs.   III

Prove that congruent chords in the same circle or in congruent circles are equidistant from the center of the circle (sphere) and apply it in solving problems and writing related proofs.   III

Use the definitions of *central angle, major arc, minor arc, semicircle, degree measure, arc addition, angular degree,* and *degree of arc* to solve related problems.   II

Prove theorems and apply them in solving problems concerning the relationship between central angles and intercepted arcs.   III

Prove that the measure of an inscribed angle is half the measure of its intercepted arc and apply this theorem in writing proofs and solving problems.   III

Prove theorems concerning the angles formed by tangents, secants, and chords and apply them to related problems and proofs.   III

Prove theorems related to the lengths of segments formed by secants and tangents and apply them to related problems and proofs.   III

Use the circumference formula, $C = 2\pi r$, the area formula, $A = \pi r^2$, and the number π to find the circumference and the area of any circle.   II

Using the formulas for the circumference and area of a circle, derive the formula for the area of a sector $\left(\dfrac{x}{360}\,\pi r^2\right.$, where x is the number of degrees in the sector), and use this formula to solve problems.   II

SECONDARY

MA 645 **Show that you can apply knowledge and techniques of coordinate geometry of the line to solving problems.** III

Plot or recognize ordered pairs and triples on a Cartesian coordinate system. II

When given two points contained in a line, use the definition of the *slope of a line* to find the slope. II

Apply the following theorem in solving problems: "Two non-vertical lines are parallel if and only if they have the same slope." III

Apply the following theorem in solving problems: "Two non-vertical lines are perpendicular if and only if the product of their slopes is equal to -1." III

Prove and apply to problems the following distance formula. III

$$dP_1P_2 = \sqrt{(x_2 - x_1)^2 + (y_2 - y_1)^2}$$

Prove and apply to problems the following midpoint formula: "If (x,y) is the midpoint of the segment with endpoints (x_1, y_1) and (x_2, y_2), then

$$x = \frac{x_1 + x_2}{2} \text{ and } y = \frac{y_1 + y_2}{2}.\text{"} \quad \text{III}$$

Apply the following theorem in solving problems: "If P is a point between P_1 and P_2 and $\dfrac{dPP_1}{dPP_2} = r$, then the coordinates of P are $\left(\dfrac{x_1 + rx_2}{1 + r}, \dfrac{y_1 + ry_2}{1 + r}\right)$. The coordinates of P_1 are (x_1, y_1) and the coordinates of P_2 are (x_2, y_2)." III

Determine sets of points satisfying any of the following and graph them: $\parallel$, $=$, $<$, $>$, or combinations thereof. III

Describe a line by an equation using the point-slope form. II

Given the equation of a line in the point-slope form, graph the line. II

Describe a line by an equation using the slope-intercept form. II

Given the equation of a line in slope-intercept form, graph the equation. II

Given a theorem to prove by coordinate geometry methods, apply the most appropriate coordinates to make the algebraic calculations as easy as possible. III

Given a theorem to prove by coordinate geometry methods, apply the most appropriate coordinates to insure that the proof is a general case, not a special case. III

Given a geometry theorem, prove the theorem by applying co-ordinate geometry definitions, theorems, and techniques. III

MA 650 **Show that you can use vectors, polar coordinates, and the polar form of complex numbers to find the solutions to analytic problems. III**

Define *vector, equivalent vectors, the sense of vectors,* and *zero vectors*. II

Multiply a vector by a real number (scalar multiplication). II

Add and subtract vectors. II

Verify (1) that addition of vectors is commutative and associative, and (2) that scalar multiplication is distributive over addition: $a(\vec{b} + \vec{c}) = \vec{ab} + \vec{ac}$. (These are not proofs.) II

Write related vector problems from word problems and solve them. III

Express in four different ways the same ordered pair (r, θ), where r is the polar distance and θ the direction angle. II

SECONDARY

In the domain of real numbers, convert a point $P(x, y)$ in the rectangular coordinate system to an equivalent point $P(r, \theta)$ in the polar coordinate system, and vice versa.   II

Given the vector 2/30°, find the rectangular components. Given the rectangular components, find the direction angle and/or the radius vector.   II

From the conversion formulas $x = r \cos \theta$ and $y = r \sin \theta$, derive the polar form $[r(\cos \theta + i \sin \theta)]$ of a complex number $(x + yi)$, and vice versa.   II

Multiply two complex numbers that are written in the polar form $r(\cos \theta)$.   II

Divide two complex numbers that are written in the polar form. II

Find and write the powers and roots of complex numbers that are written in polar form (De Moivre's Theorem).   II

Derive the trigonometric series for the sin x and cos x when given the exponential series

$$\lim_{n \to \infty} \left(1 + \frac{x}{n}\right)^n = 1 + x + \frac{x^2}{2!} + \frac{x^3}{3!} + \frac{x^4}{4!} \ldots = e^x$$

and from De Moivre's Theorem

$$\cos x + i \sin x = \left(\cos \frac{x}{n} + i \sin \frac{x}{n}\right)^n$$

where $r = 1$ and n is a positive number. Use these series to solve related problems.   II

MA 655   Show that you can derive the equations of conic sections and solve related problems.   III

Describe conditions for which $Ax^2 + Bxy + Cy^2 + Dx + Ey + F = 0$ is a circle (including the null circle) and solve related problems.   II

Determine the equation of the circle from the conditions that determine it and solve related problems, including the "nine-point circle" of triangles.   III

Determine the standard form of the equation of the parabola, including that which is rotated 90°, and solve related problems.   III

Find the equation of a parabola whose axis is oblique.   II

List at least five applications of parabolas.   I

Explain the terms *major axis, minor axis, foci, eccentricity,* and *latus rectum* as they relate to ellipses and solve related problems.   II

Determine the standard form of an ellipse whose center is not at the origin and solve related problems.   III

Solve problems related to ellipses with oblique axes.   II

List at least five applications of ellipses.   I

Define and use the following terms and solve related problems: (1) *length of latus rectum* $= \dfrac{2b^2}{a}$; (2) $\epsilon = \dfrac{c}{a}$, $c > a$; (3) *asymptotes;* (4) *standard equation;* (5) *foci;* (6) *vertex;* (7) *center;* (8) *transverse axis;* (9) *conjugate axis;* and (10) *hyperbola.*   II

Determine the general form of the equation for a hyperbola and write equations for hyperbolas whose centers are not at the origin.   III

Determine equations of rectangular hyperbolas and hyperbolas with oblique axes.   III

List at least five applications of hyperbolas.   I

Determine the three conics in terms of the value of the eccentricity.   III

SECONDARY

Using rotation equations, rewrite quadratic equations, eliminating the xy term.   II

Using the trigonometric form of rotation equations, rewrite quadratic equations to eliminate the xy term.   II

Given any quadratic equation in two variables, describe its graph.   II

MA 660   Show that you can find the curve of best fit for two tables of values.   III

Describe the line of best fit for a table of values.   II

Find the curve ($y = ax^n$) of best fit for a table of values. (Logarithmic paper is needed.)   II

Find a polynomial equation ($y = a + bx + cx^2$) of best fit for a table of values.   II

MA 665   Solve problems relating to the areas or volumes of solids.   III

Apply the theorem related to areas of cross-sections of prisms to solve related problems.   III

Prove theorems related to the lateral face, lateral surface, and total surface of prisms and apply these theorems to solve problems.   III

Use theorems concerning cross-sectional area in a pyramid and in pyramids with the same base, area, and altitude to find the area of various cross-sections of a pyramid.   II

Define Cavalieri's principle and find the volume of a prism using the formula $V = bh$ and the volume of a pyramid using the formula $V = \frac{1}{3}bh$.   II

Find the volume of a circular cylinder using the formula $V = bh$ and the volume of a circular cone using the formula $V = \frac{1}{3}bh$.   II

Find the volume and surface area of a sphere using the formulas $V = \frac{4}{3}\pi r^3$ and $S = 4\pi r^2$.   II

MA 670 **Show that you can use the definitions and formulas of plane and solid analytic geometry to solve problems involving points, line, planes, and surfaces.   III**

Given two points $A(x_1, y_1)$ and $B(x_2, y_2)$, find the coordinates of a point P between A and B such that $\frac{AP}{BP} = r$ where r is a rational number.   II

Determine a formula for the area of a convex polygon in terms of the coordinates of the vertices, and use the formula to solve related problems.   III

Find the angle ϕ from line l_1 to line l_2 if l_1 and l_2 intersect and neither l_1 nor l_2 is vertical.   II

Given a word description characterizing the path of a point, find the equation that describes the path.   II

Use the general equation of a line to solve related problems.   II
1. $Ax + By + C = 0$
2. The normal form, $\dfrac{Ax + By + C}{\pm\sqrt{A^2 + B^2}} = 0$
3. The distance (d) of a point $P(x_1, y_1)$ not on the line where $d = \dfrac{\pm Ax_1 + By_1 + C}{\sqrt{A^2 + B^2}}$

To solve problems about normals, use the equation $x \cos w + y \sin w + \rho = 0$ where w is the angle of inclination of the normal to line l and ρ is the distance from l to the origin.   II

Determine the distance and midpoint formulas for 3-space paths and solve related problems.   III

Use direction cosines and direction numbers to solve related problems.   II

SECONDARY

Find the angle between two lines.   II

Find the direction numbers of a line perpendicular to two skew lines.   II

Find the equation of a plane perpendicular to a given line at a given point.   II

Find the angle between two given planes.   II

Find the distance from a point to a plane.   II

Find the equation of a plane represented by three given points.   II

Determine parametric, symmetric, general equations, and projecting planes of lines through two given points, and solve related problems.   III

Given two conditions that determine a line, find the equation of the line.   II

Find the equation of a sphere, and solve related problems.   II

Solve word problems relating to ellipsoids, hyperboloids of one or two sheets, elliptic paraboloids, hyperbolic paraboloids, and elliptic cones.   III

Use rectangular, cylindrical, or spherical coordinates to solve related word problems.   III

measurement and Probability

MA 675   Show that you can apply probability theory to solve word problems.   III

Apply the concept of the Cartesian product or the fundamental counting principle to solve problems involving permutations for *n* objects, all of which are different.   III

Solve problems using the formula for the number of permutations of *n* objects, not all of which are different.   III

Derive the formula for finding the number of combinations of *n* elements taken *r* at a time ($_nC_r$).   II

Find the number of combinations of *n* elements taken *r* at a time ($_nC_r$).   II

Solve combination-permutation word problems.   III

Considering a sample space with equally likely outcomes, solve word problems involving single-event probability.   III

Solve word problems involving the probability of mutually exclusive events.   III

Solve word problems involving the probability of independent and dependent events.   III

seTs anD LOGIC

MA 680   Show that you can construct deductive proof or proof by mathematical induction.   III

Define the following terms as related to the concept of proof: *axioms, (postulates), definitions, reflexive, symmetric, transitive, substitution, theorem, equivalence.*   II

Write formal proofs of real number theorems using the properties of real numbers.   III

Apply mathematical induction in proving or disproving conjectures about the natural numbers.   III

SECONDARY

MA 685 **Show that you can construct derivations or proofs of differentiation formulas or of theorems of differential and integral calculus. III**

Define the derivative of a function and identify common notations for it. II

Using the definition of derivative, develop formulas for differentiating the following types of functions. V
1. $y = x^n$ where n is a positive integer.
2. $y = cu$ where c is a constant and u is a differentiable function.
3. $y = u + v$ where u and v are differentiable functions.
4. $y = u \cdot v$ where u and v are differentiable functions.
5. $y = \dfrac{u}{v}$ where u and v are differentiable functions.

Given an incomplete proof of the derivation of the formula for $\dfrac{d}{du}$ (sin u), find the missing details. II

Given the formula for $\dfrac{d}{du}$ (sin u), find derivations for $\dfrac{d}{du}$ (cos u) and for $\dfrac{d}{du}$ (tan u). II

Given an incomplete proof of the derivations for $\dfrac{d}{du}$ (arc sin u), $\dfrac{d}{du}$ (arc cos u), and $\dfrac{d}{du}$ (arc tan u), find the missing details. II

Demonstrate an understanding of Rolle's Theorem by illustrating it geometrically. III

Demonstrate an understanding of the mean-value theorem by illustrating it geometrically. III

Given an incomplete proof of the mean-value theorem, find the missing details. II

Define integration to be the determination of an antiderivative. II

Define the definite integral to be the limit of a sum.   II

Prove and use the Fundamental Theorem of integral calculus.   III

Develop and use the following properties of the definite integral.
V

1. $\int_a^b [f(x) + g(x)] \, dx = \int_a^b f(x) \, dx + \int_a^b g(x) \, dx$

2. $\int_a^b cf(x) \, dx = c \int_a^b f(x) \, dx$

3. $\int_a^b f(x) \, dx = \int_a^c f(x) \, dx + \int_c^b f(x) \, dx$ where $a < c < b$.

4. If $F(x) = \int_a^x f(t) \, dt$, then $F'(x) = f(x)$.

PROBLEM SOLVING

MA 690 **Show that you can solve consumer problems by applying knowledge of arithmetic operations, decimals, and percentage.   III**

Find the simple interest when the principal and the rate of interest are known.   II

Find the compound interest when the time, the principal, and the rate are given.   II

Given a number and an interest rate and using simple and compound interest tables, find the simple and compound interest.   II

Solve word problems involving simple and compound interest.   III

Define the terms *charge account* and *revolving charge account* and describe the advantages and disadvantages of each.   II

Given an unpaid balance on a revolving charge account with a 1% interest charge and the amount of the monthly payment, determine the total amount to be paid.   III

SECONDARY

Given the price of an article, the amount of each monthly payment, and the total number of payments, determine the service charge and the rate of simple interest represented by the service charge. III

Given the price of an article, the amount of each payment on an installment plan, and the number of payments on the installment plan, determine the total cost to buyers. Determine this if cost is more or less than the cost if cash were borrowed from a bank for the same period of time at a given interest rate. III

Given a bank's interest rate, a credit union's interest rate, and an amount of money to be borrowed, determine whether a loan from the bank or one from the credit union would cost less. III

Given the beginning date of a loan and the length of time until the loan must be repaid, determine the date of maturity of the loan. III

Given the amount of a loan, the rate of discount, and the length of time until the loan must be repaid, determine the bank discount and the proceeds. III

Define and give an example of the following terms: *commission, net proceeds, sales,* and *rate of commission.* II

Determine the amount of commission when the total sales and the rate based on total sales are known. III

Given the total sales and the amount of commission, determine the net proceeds. III

Given the total sales and the amount of commission, determine the rate of commission. III

Define and give an example of the terms *marked price* (list price), *discount,* and *net price.* II

Determine the net price when the list price and the discount rate are known. III

Determine the discount when the list price and the discount rate are known. III

Determine the rate of discount when the list price and the discount are known.   III

Determine the discount and the rate of discount when the list price and the net price are given.   III

Define and give an example of the following terms: *profit, loss, margin, overhead, selling price,* and *cost.*   II

Given the cost of an article and its selling price, determine the margin.   III

Given the cost of an article, the selling price, and the overhead, determine the profit or the loss.   III

Given the cost of an article and the profit, find the percent of profit on the cost.   II

Given the cost and the percent of margin on the cost, determine the margin and the selling price.   III

Define and give an example of *income tax.*   II

Given a weekly salary and the number of exemptions, determine the income-tax deduction.   III

Given the necessary information, complete a W-4 Withholding Exemption Form.   II

Given an annual salary, the total tax deduction, and the number of exemptions, complete Form 1040-A.   II

Given a salary and the percent of deduction, find the amount of social security to be contributed by the employee.   II

Given the price of an article and the rate of sales tax, find the amount of tax and the total selling price.   II

Given the total price of an article and the amount of the tax, find the rate of sales tax.   II

SECONDARY

Given the assessed value of the property, find the property tax when the rate is expressed in dollars per $100 or per $1000 of assessed valuation. II

Given the assessed value of the property, find the property tax when the rate is expressed in mills or cents per $1.00 of assessed valuation or when the rate is expressed as a percent of the assessed valuation. II

Given the necessary information, complete a deposit slip for a checking account. II

Given transactions that have taken place, calculate the new balance for a checking account on the check stub or on a balance sheet. II

Given transactions that have taken place, complete a savings-account passbook. II

Given the annual interest rate, determine the interest on a specified amount of savings for a specified period of time. III

Determine the amount of interest and the new balance for a savings account when a given amount of money is left in an account for a given period of time at a given rate of interest. III

MA 695   Show that you can apply integral calculus to the solution of practical problems from geometry, physics, or everyday life.   III

Relate integration to the problem of finding the area under a curve. II

Using integration, determine the area under a given curve or between two given curves. III

Using integration, determine the length of a given curve. III

Using integration, determine the volume of a given solid of revolution. III

Using integration, find the average value of a function over a given domain. II

Use integration in solving work problems from physics.   II

Given the velocity or the acceleration as a function of time and given the initial conditions, apply indefinite integration to find distance as a function of time.   III

Use the differential equation $y' = ky$ to solve word problems involving growth or decay.   III

MA 700 **Show that you can apply differential calculus to the solution of practical problems from geometry, physics, or everyday life.** **III**

Using the concept of a limit, find the slope of a given polynomial function at a given point.   II

Find the nth derivative of a given rational function.   II

Graph a given function by using the first derivative to determine the direction of the curve and by using the first and second derivatives to locate relative maximum points, relative minimum points, and points of inflection.   II

Using first and second derivatives, solve maximization and minimization problems.   II

Using the first and second derivatives, solve related rate and motion problems.   II

Solve word problems that require the differentiation of trigonometric or inverse trigonometric functions.   III

Given a function and the endpoints of an interval, determine a point c within the interval that satisfies the mean-value theorem.   III

TERMINAL OBJECTIVES

aPPenDIx

TERMINAL OBJECTIVES

analysis of number and system

PRIMARY

MA 005   Show that you can use arabic numerals to count objects and words.   III

MA 010   Show that you can use place value to 9999.   II

MA 015   Show your understanding of the relationship of roman numerals to arabic numerals.   II

INTERMEDIATE

MA 200   Show that you can use early number systems by expressing symbols of one system in symbols of another system.   III

MA 205   Show that you can use place value to 10 digits.   III

MA 210   Show that you can identify the properties of whole numbers and apply these properties to problems.   III

MA 215   Show that you can apply the techniques necessary to write mathematical expressions in simplest terms.   III

MA 220   Show your understanding of proper and improper fractions.   II

MA 225   Show that you can apply an understanding of equivalent fractions.   III

MA 230   Show your understanding of prime and composite numbers.   II

MA 235   Show your understanding of absolute values.   II

TERMINAL OBJECTIVES

MA 240   Show your understanding of rational and irrational numbers.   II

MA 245   Show that you can use exponential notation.   II

MA 250   Show your understanding of expanded and scientific notation.   II

SECONDARY

MA 500   Show that you can use arithmetic operations on whole numbers, fractions, and decimals to solve given problems.   III

MA 505   Show that you can solve problems requiring the use of properties of real numbers or of complex numbers.   III

MA 510   Show that you can solve problems requiring the use of properties of arithmetic, geometric, and binomial expansions.   III

OPERATIONS: NUMERICAL AND ALGEBRAIC

PRIMARY

MA 020   Show that you can use addition to add 4-digit numbers.   III

MA 025   Show that you can use subtraction to perform operations with 4-digit numbers.   III

MA 030   Show that you can use multiplication facts.   III

MA 035   Show that you can use division to solve problems with 1-digit divisors.   III

MA 040   Show that you can use addition to add like fractions.   III

TERMINAL OBJECTIVES

INTERMEDIATE

MA 255   Show that you can add and subtract 4-digit numbers. III

MA 260   Show that you can solve multiplication problems with at least 2-digit multipliers. III

MA 265   Show that you can solve division problems with at least 2-digit divisors. III

MA 270   Show your understanding of estimating answers to problems. II

MA 275   Show that you can complete operations on integers. II

MA 280   Show that you can add and subtract fractions. III

MA 285   Show that you can multiply and divide fractions. III

MA 290   Show that you can demonstrate conversion methods for fractions and decimals. III

MA 300   Show that you can add and subtract decimals. III

MA 305   Show that you can multiply and divide decimals. III

MA 310   Show that you can solve problems in ratio. III

MA 315   Show that you can solve problems in percentage. III

MA 320   Show that you can perform square-root operations by finding the square root of a number. II

MA 325   Show that you can perform operations on bases other than 10. III

MA 330   Show that you can apply elements of finite and non-finite mathematical systems. III

SECONDARY

MA 515   Show that you can solve simple linear equations.   III

MA 520   Show that you can solve word problems by using algebraic equations.   III

MA 525   Show that you can perform basic algebraic operations and simplifications including factoring.   III

MA 530   Show that you can solve word problems by using algebraic techniques.   III

MA 535   Show that you can solve equations and inequalities including linear and quadratic systems and polynomial equations.   III

MA 540   Show that you can perform complex algebraic operations and simplifications.   III

MA 545   Show that you can find the derivative of an algebraic, trigonometric, inverse trigonometric, exponential, or logarithmic function.   III

MA 550   Show that you can apply knowledge of the properties and functions and limits without reference to calculus. III

MA 555   Show that you can apply methods of calculus or numerical analysis to the approximation of functional values, transcendental functions, and definite integrals. III

Operations: Graphics

PRIMARY

MA 045   Show your understanding of given patterns by reproducing them.   II

MA 050   Show your understanding of functions of graphs by explaining them.   II

TERMINAL OBJECTIVES

INTERMEDIATE

MA 335   Show that you can prepare flow charts to solve given algorithms.   III

MA 340   Show that you can explain data presented in graphs and construct graphs to summarize data.   III

MA 345   Show your understanding of graph relations and functions.   II

SECONDARY

MA 560   Show that you can apply the definitions, relationships, and theorems of numerical trigonometry to the solution of problems.   III

MA 565   Show that you can find the derivative of an algebraic, trigonometric, inverse trigonometric, exponential, or logarithmic function.   III

MA 570   Show that you can derive and use the multiple-angle formulas to prove that an equation is an identity and to solve an equation.   III

MA 575   Show that you can use the definitions of the circular functions and their inverses to graph and to solve analytic problems.   III

MA 580   Show that you can graph plane curves specified in rectangular or polar coordinates, including those given by parametric equations.   III

MA 585   Show that you can graph truth sets of quadratic equations and inequalities and that you can graph functions and relations.   III

MA 590   Show that you can find the integral of an algebraic or transcendental function by using a basic integration formula or a standard technique of integration.   III

TERMINAL OBJECTIVES

MA 595   Show that you can graph relations and functions and find equations of relations and functions, both linear and quadratic.   III

MA 600   Show that you can solve problems requiring the use of properties of exponential, logarithmic, linear, and quadratic functions.   III

Geometry

PRIMARY

MA 055   Show your understanding of geometric figures and circles by recognizing them.   II

INTERMEDIATE

MA 350   Show your understanding of points, lines, angles, and planes by recognizing them.   II

MA 355   Show that you understand the properties and classifications of geometric figures by describing them.   II

MA 360   Show that you can construct and measure geometric figures and models.   III

MA 365   Show your understanding of geometric figures by finding their perimeter, area, and volume.   II

MA 370   Show that you can demonstrate and apply the Pythagorean Relationship.   III

SECONDARY

MA 605   Using formulas, solve word problems that require finding the perimeters, areas, and volumes of geometric shapes.   III

TERMINAL OBJECTIVES

MA 610   Show that you can construct geometric figures using a compass and unmarked straightedge.   III

MA 615   Show that you can apply the Pythagorean Theorem, the concept of similar triangles, or trigonometric ratios to make indirect measurements.   II

MA 620   Show that you can construct deductive and indirect proofs and proofs using coordinate geometry.   II

MA 625   Apply definitions and properties of angles and triangles to the solution of problems.   III

MA 630   Apply definitions and properties of lines and planes to the solution of problems.   III

MA 635   Apply definitions and properties of quadrilaterals and other polygons to the solution of problems.   III

MA 640   Show that you can apply definitions and properties of circles to the solution of problems.   III

MA 645   Show that you can apply knowledge and techniques of coordinate geometry of the line to solving problems. III

MA 650   Show that you can use vectors, polar coordinates, and the polar form of complex numbers to find the solutions to analytic problems.   III

MA 655   Show that you can derive the equations of conic sections and solve related problems.   III

MA 660   Show that you can find the curve of best fit for two tables of values.   III

MA 665   Solve problems relating to the areas or volumes of solids.   III

MA 670   Show that you can use the definitions and formulas of plane and solid analytic geometry to solve problems involving points, line, planes, and surfaces.   III

measurement and probability

PRIMARY

MA 060   Show that you can use coin values.   III

MA 065   Show that you can apply understanding of time to the minute.   III

MA 070   Show that you can use linear measure to 1/4 inch.   III

MA 075   Show your understanding of temperature readings.   II

MA 080   Show your understanding of weight and liquid measurements.   II

INTERMEDIATE

MA 375   Show that you can demonstrate exactness of measurement.   III

MA 380   Show that you can convert one system of measurement to another system.   III

MA 385   Show that you can use addition and subtraction with measures of time, weight, and capacity.   II

MA 390   Show that you can demonstrate the theory of probability.   III

MA 400   Show that you can apply the frequencies and measures of central tendency.   III

SECONDARY

MA 675   Show that you can apply probability theory to solve word problems.   III

TERMINAL OBJECTIVES

seTS anD LOGIC

PRIMARY

MA 085 Show that you can use facts pertaining to elements of a set. III

MA 090 Show that you can use set notation to solve simple problems. III

INTERMEDIATE

MA 405 Show that you can demonstrate sets and set notation. III

MA 410 Show your understanding of the rudiments of logic as they relate to mathematics. II

MA 415 Demonstrate your ability to combine principles, concepts, and generalization by developing an original finite mathematical system, by listing a set of elements, and by defining an operation on the set for which the set is closed and one for which the set is not closed. V

SECONDARY

MA 680 Show that you can construct deductive proof or proof by mathematical induction. III

MA 685 Show that you can construct derivations or proofs of differentiation formulas or of theorems of differential and integral calculus. III

PROBLeM SOLVING

PRIMARY

MA 095 Show that you can write number sentences (equations). III

MATHEMATICS

MA 100   Show that you can solve simple word problems.   III

MA 105   Show that you can write and solve number sentences for simple word problems.   III

INTERMEDIATE

MA 420   Show that you can write and solve equations for word problems.   III

MA 425   Show that you can solve word problems relating to consumer needs.   III

MA 430   Show that you can solve problems relating to consumer living.   III

MA 435   Show that you can apply mathematical operations to problems dealing with sports.   III

MA 440   Show that you can apply mathematical operations to problems dealing with occupations and future education.   III

SECONDARY

MA 690   Show that you can solve consumer problems by applying knowledge of arithmetic operations, decimals, and percentage.   III

MA 695   Show that you can apply integral calculus to the solution of practical problems from geometry, physics, or everyday life.   III

MA 700   Show that you can apply differential calculus to the solution of practical problems from geometry, physics, or everyday life.   III

InDex

INDEX

INDEX

INDEX

DuBois, W. E. B., SS:76
Duty, SS:44

Ear, SC:1, 13
Early civilizations, SS:52, 78, 85
Earth, SC:8
Earth, changes in, SC:76–77
Earth, composition of, SC:75–76
Earthquake activity, SC:77
Earth science, intermediate level, SC:39–40
Earth science, primary level, SC:8–9
Earth science, secondary level, SC:75–80
Ecology, SC:56; SS:33, 54–56, 87
Economic concepts and terms, SS:58
Economic development, SS:170
Economics, intermediate level, SS:56–62
Economics, primary level, SS:9–15
Economics, secondary level, SS:121–130
Economic systems, SS:58–59, 81, 82, 126
Economics, personal, SS:60
Editorial writing, SS:69
Education, SS:30, 135
Education, colonial, SS:18
Einstein, Albert, SC:57
Elections, SS:5, 94–95
Electrical circuit, SC:7
Electric bill, MA:46; SS:60
Electric charges, SC:70–71
Electric circuits, SC:71
Electric current, SC:34, 71
Electricity, SC:33
Electrochemistry, SC:62
Electrolysis, SC:71
Electrolytic process, SC:62
Electromagnet, SC:34
Electromagnetic induction, SC:72–73
Electromagnetic theory of light, SC:70
Electron, SC:27, 28
Electron configuration, SC:74
Electronic components, SC:34
Element, SC:27, 28, 57, 75
Elizabethan drama, LA:88
Embryos, development, SC:50
Encyclopedia, SS:140; LA:42
Endocrine glands, SC:12
Endocrine system, SC:52

INDEX

INDEX

INDEX

INDEX

INDEX

INDEX

INDEX

INDEX

BeHavioraL OBJecTives

A Guide to Individualizing Learning

Text: Videocomp 9 point Roma with 10 point Roma Bold, display lines in 14 point Dimensia

Design and art: Steven Jacobs Design, Palo Alto, California

Editorial and production: Westinghouse Learning Press, Palo Alto, California

Composition, lithography, binding, packaging: Kingsport Press, Kingsport, Tennessee